TAO TE JINX

TAO TE JINX

THE COLLECTED APHORISMS & QUOTATIONS OF

Steve Aylett

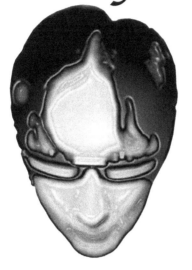

www.rawdogscreaming.com

Introduction and interior design by D. Harlan Wilson
www.dharlanwilson.com

Cover design by Matthew Revert
www.matthewrevert.com

Anti-Oedipus Press
Grand Rapids, MI

@AntiOedipusP
@antioedipuspress

www.anti-oedipuspress.com

BOOKS BY STEVE AYLETT

Novels
The Crime Studio
Bigot Hall
Slaughtermatic
The Inflatable Volunteer
Atom
Shamanspace
Lint
Fain the Sorcerer
Rebel at the End of Time
Novahead

The Complete Accomplice
Only An Alligator
The Velocity Gospel
Dummyland
Karloff's Circus

Collections
Toxicology
And Your Point Is?
Smithereens

Comics
The Nerve
The Caterer
Get that Thing Away from Me
Johnny Viable and His Terse Friends
Hyperthick

Nonfiction
Heart of the Original

Other Media
Lord Pin
The Promissory

For Sophie and Hans.

ON READING NEW BOOKS

Enjoyment can be kept sharp by the outrage of others. Sadly, though, genuinely-felt outrage is as rare today as it's ever been. I rode out of a swirling vortex on a hell-pig the other day and people just stared. It's a world where things created for comfort are used for denial and the dwindling comb-over of culture has led to books in which the protagonist is one or other kind of automated remnant. The inherent advantage of selling limitation is that one size is declared to fit all. Support is minimal for defiance in a world with charity toward none, malice for all, and the bland decree that there can be no new ideas under the local sun. When offered a handful of options by a manipulator, we should be careful (in turning directly away to look at the thousands of other options available) that we are not being cleverly positioned to miss the billions more in every other direction. The truly new invents new guts for itself. An angel is unlikely to be boring or devout. The miraculous should be at least equal to the forbidden. Imagine the horror of dropping into the world's throat while trusting others' declarations above the evidence of your own senses!

—*Steve Aylett, 2001*

STEVE AYLETT

LINT

S N O W B O O K S

"THE MOST ORIGINAL VOICE ON THE LITERARY SCENE" *MICHAEL MOORCOCK*

INTRODUCTION
The Tao of Aylett
D. HARLAN WILSON

I discovered Steve Aylett the same year that I sold my first story, "An Unleashing," in 1999. I had been submitting fiction to magazines since 1995 and accumulated an impressive stockpile of rejection letters. Back then, most correspondence between authors and editors took place by standard mail, and most publications were in print. There weren't many online venues. What did exist left much to be desired in terms of quality. I didn't care. I just wanted to get published, and I cast a wide net.

I received $20 for "An Unleashing" from a new online magazine called *Liquid Fiction* that tanked after its first issue, evaporating from the internet like an evicted demon. So be it. Now I was on my way as an author, and clearly people were starting to recognize the value and dynamism of my creative efforts. In the event that somebody doubted me, I printed out the issue and enclosed it in an eelskin binder to prove that I was a published author.

I don't know what happened to that printout, and I don't really remember much about "An Unleashing" other than the setting (Liverpool) and what happens in the end (a guy yanks on his tongue and turns himself inside-out). I do remember how high on the hog I felt, and when I sold my second story, "The Fire Drill," that same year to another online magazine, *Akkadian*, the hog exploded beneath the weight of my ego. It didn't matter to me that *Akkadian* only paid me $15 and also died on the vine after its inaugural issue. I was obviously special, and at least *two* editors thought so. That's a multitude. That's a readership.

During the early period of my writing career, I was jealous of authors who had published novels. I spent hours in bookstores sifting through the shelves and reassuring myself that my writing was just as good as (and usually better than) all these recycled, canned excuses for "literature." These goddamned books were dogshit compared to what I knew I could and would accomplish. Where this inane, irrational, decidedly *untrue* self-confidence came from—I have no idea beyond the notion that the narcissistic engine of my insecurities was turbo-charged and possessed ample horsepower. I had started several novels and finished none of them. Each abandoned project was a learning experience, I told myself, but I'm not sure how I figured that I was better than almost every living author. Perhaps this has to do with why I mainly read dead authors today. Whatever the case, I created a fiction about my own authorship long before I became a bona fide "author."

This fiction vaporized the moment I began to read Aylett's *Slaughtermatic* (1997).

I found it in the science-fiction section of Schuler's Bookstore in East Lansing, Michigan, where I had just started my Ph.D. at Michigan State University. The minimalist cover foregrounded a simple, spattered bloodstain. Intrigued, I read the first sentence: "Beerlight was a blown circuit, where to kill a man was less a murder than a mannerism" (1). It reminded me of the first sentence of William Gibson's *Neuromancer* (1984): "The sky above the port was the color of television, tuned to a dead channel" (3). Gibson's legendary opener has been written about at length; the assertion concisely, "neuromantically" sets the tone for the entire novel while thematizing the darkly technological environment of Gibson's cyberpunk world. Aylett's opener does something similar, but it also points to the ultraviolence and absurdity that distinguishes the postcyberpunk world of Beerlight. I kept reading, and a few pages later, I was hooked. I sat down in a nearby café and finished *Slaughtermatic* in one sitting—a great rarity for me to this day.

As I read, my emotions oscillated between enmity and reverence for the author's wizardly execution, prowess, and prose. Who was this dirty son of a bitch? I was used to picking up books and hastily picking them apart, sentence by sentence, word by word, but my sensibilities failed me. I couldn't find the usual flaws. I couldn't find any flaws. It was as if *Slaughtermatic* dared me to critique it, knowing that I would fail to bring my juvenile, insecure modus to bear. In part, my mania stemmed from the wry self-reflexivity that typifies all of Aylett's writing, but the novel did much more than call attention to itself in interesting ways. I had been reading an excess of literary theory, and an aphorism from Jean François Lyotard's *The Postmodern Condition* (1979) immediately leapt to mind: "To speak is to fight" (10). Every page of *Slaughtermatic* was a cunning, "slaughtermatic" punch that displaced readers from their comfort zones and jeopardized the authority of the bottled, formulaic, predictable fiction that dominated the market.

What qualifies as popular "literature" today isn't literary at all, although it's plagued by the same blasé affect that distinguishes contemporary "literary fiction." It's no wonder that most people, if they read at all, get their material from Walmart and service plazas. Popular fiction hinges on spoonfed narrative and shitheel prose. Literary fiction tries too hard to be clever, intellectual, and lyrical. And a specter is haunting both genres—the specter of terminal ennui.

I'm not saying that Aylett isn't "literary" nor "popular." He's both. Unlike most authors, however, he siphons the best essences of those genres, combining singular, effervescent rhetoric with characters and "action sequences" that defy our expectations and remind us of who we are, where we've been, and where we're going. We're going right into the shitter, of course, as our pornoviolent desires continue to leak from our mindscreens into the real world with greater intensity and force of madness. *Humanity will be the death of humanity*—Aylett loves to play with this apocalyptic theme, and the humor with which he enacts it has become one of his signatures. Like William S. Burroughs, his fiction can function as a kind of standup routine wherein the narrator roasts characters as much as readers, sometimes subtly, sometimes overtly.

In addition to synthesizing literary, popular, and comedic modes of storytelling, Aylett wanders like an unbound nomad into other genres, namely science fiction, fantasy, irrealism, and neonoir. His fiction is multigeneric in the strictest sense, as if his imagination refuses to be categorized and pinned down. It certainly refuses to follow the rules of what any masterclass, MFA program, or how-to textbook will tell you constitutes "good" writing. This is why Aylett is one of the only great living writers. Technically, I should hate him. And yet I can't stop reading and rereading him, even though he has variably professed to be moribund (i.e., "retired") while releasing original work now and then, such as the extraordinary three-issue comic *Hyperthick* (2022), selections of which appear in this latest edition of *Tao Te Jinx*. More on that front shortly.

After reading *Slaughtermatic*, I went on the hunt for other books by Aylett. He's a prolific author, but at the time, he had only written two other novels, *The Crime Studio* (1994) and *Bigot Hall* (1995). I couldn't find anything about them on the proto-internet; it would be a few years before eBay and then Amazon conquered the bookselling universe.

Thankfully, Aylett's fourth book, *Toxicology* (1999), a short-fiction collection, soon appeared on Schuler's shelves. I had been writing a lot of my own short stories, and I thought some of them were pretty good, but like *Slaughtermatic*, *Toxicology* served me another slice of humble pie and ratcheted down my hubris a few more notches. Kafka's parables had been a source of inspiration for my flash fiction, and I was excited to read Aylett's flash-parable "The Met Are All for This," a sardonic science-fictionalization of *The Metamorphosis* (1915) whose protagonist, Menwith Usansa, has "a tarnished crust of infinity receivers coat[ing] his skin," "a discreet pinhole camcorder embedded in his forehead," and "a quartz-controlled ultra-high frequency transmitter up each nostril" (121). I was as upset as I was excited. Aylett was doing what I wanted to do, but I lacked the experience, skill, and vision to pull off. He had anticipated a future version of myself that would only come to fruition in an alternate universe. Or something like that—I used to believe in much more than Being and Nothingness. Regardless, I felt an affinity with this talented bastard, and I still do. Right now, in fact, I can feel his words skewering the tight-assed academic style of this very introduction even as those words massage the knots out of my frontal lobe …

In the first decade of the twenty-first century, Aylett's canon grew larger at a rapid pace, with books like *Atom* (2000), *Shamanspace* (2001), and the four-volume Accomplice series, including *Only an Alli-*

gator (2001), *The Velocity Gospel* (2002), *Dummyland* (2002), and *Karloff's Circus* (2004). Every book was unique yet distinctly Aylettesque, and each one exhibited a subtextual aesthetic aggression, an embedded "velocity gospel" that saw Aylett attempt to outwrite and outperform the younger versions of himself. This effort came to a head in his magnum opus, *Lint* (2005), a riotous, meta-satirical hagiography about faux pulp-SF trickster Jeff Lint, who Aylett says "cut a frayed figure in the world [and was] a man who voluntarily spoke the truth on countless occasions, who lived for love of unnamed colors and the glee of releasing vertical bombs of resentment" (195-96). Many literary critics and science-fiction scholars have debated whether or not Lint's antics are mere symptoms of Aylett's broken karma, but such biographical considerations miss the point. *Lint* imparts more about the fundamental idiocy of writers, publishers, readers, editors, and ultimately human beings than it does about the author or the titular provocateur, and the book remains unlike anything I've ever read.

Thereafter, Aylett's publications became more sporadic but no less innovative and impactful. Among them is *The Caterer* (2008), a one-issue comic "written" by Lint; according to the back-cover copy, this "holy barnacle of failure," as Alan Moore refers to it, single-handedly wrecked his ersatz career. The farcical implosion of reality and fiction is another Aylett signature that he teased out further in *And Your Point Is?* (2014), a collection of essays and reviews devoted to "the rigors of Lint's flaying, vortical screeds" (9), as well as novels like *Rebel at the End of Time* (2011), *Fain the Sorcerer* (2012), and *Novahead* (2011), the final installment in the Beerlight series initiated by *The Crime Studio*. I wrote an article on *Novahead* called "Goodbye, Beerlight" that appeared in 2016 in the first anthology of literary criticism published on Aylett's oeuvre. Permit me to channel my own distillate with impunity. In the article, I hypothesize:

> If *Novahead* had a thesis, it might be this statement uttered by bartender Don Toto: "Violence longs to be repeated merely— somehow it's never bored" (67). This is precisely what Aylett's novel does, showing not only how violence is never bored, but never *boring*. He stylizes violence and renders it an art form in

> terms of the images he depicts, the ideas he conjures, and the
> melodically pyrotechnic language he uses to express those im-
> ages and ideas. An expert metanarrationalist, Aylett is a writer's
> writer and a reader's friendly neighborhood recalcitrant. *Nova-
> head* not only tells a story; it thinks its way through the telling of a
> story, assessing its own machinery as well as the science-fictional
> machinery (predominantly cyberpunk) it borrows from and builds
> upon, and the American machinery it simultaneously lionizes and
> denigrates. (113)

Aylett punctuates Lyotard's directive that *to speak is to fight*, but violence in all of its literal, figurative, psychological, and aesthetic manifes-
tations neither embodies nor embrains his evolving legacy, which, like
the cinema of Stanley Kubrick and David Lynch, thrives on calculated
misdirection and the gleeful cultivation of ambiguity.

In *The Impossible David Lynch* (2007), Todd McGowan makes a case
for fantasy operating as the "reality-support" of the auteur's diegeses
and, by extension, the diegesis of viewers. Lynch's films, in other words,
collapse the boundaries between spectator and screen; as such, they un-
derscore how fantasy is not just a mindless escape from the real world,
but a device for reconstructing and revolutionizing the social, psychological, and ideological fabric of reality. "The greatness of a work of art
depends on its ability to transform the audience," McGowan claims, and
"it is in this sense that Lynch is 'weird': one cannot watch a Lynch film in
the way that one watches a standard Hollywood film nor in the way that
one watches most radical films. The structure of a Lynch film challenges
the spectator's traditional experience of the cinema just as it engages
and challenges the history of film theory" (1, 2). Correspondingly, the
structure of Aylett's stories and novels challenges readers and puts the
nature of reading and the history of literature in question. This is the
heartbeat of his originality, and it informs his ostensible desire to out-
Aylett himself. "Write every story as if it was your last, whether suicide
note or proof of life," he professes in the appropriately titled *Heart of
the Original*, a "secret history" of human creativity and imagination (4).

Would that more authors did likewise instead of idly occupying the
shadow of The Writing Dead. Then again, most authors couldn't find

the sand to write against the grain if they even mustered the inclination. Don't get me wrong. There's a place for shitty fiction. Look at all of the shitty readers. I'm actually amazed if somebody reads anything beyond email and the daily news. But I could do with a bit less literature that, as Aylett says in "Stingray Valentine," the introduction to my post-cyberpunk novel *Codename Prague*, uses "as many words as possible to say nothing we don't already know" (20). There's so much to be said for the concerted pursuit of innovation. Groping for the New has rendered the better angels and demons of literary history, but there's barely a pace or pulse anymore, let alone wings and horns. "Faced with an industry impermeable to talent," Aylett observes, "real creators will turn in another direction and aim at a heightened target, a unique emblem all bedecked with resinous blossoms and chained fruit" (ibid.).

Today, the resinous blossoms and chained fruits of Aylett's output come to us in ever more inimitable forms. Along with *Hyperthick*, for instance, he recently published a deck of Tarot cards. I don't know if he does his own artwork, but it's a beautiful set containing the usual cartomantic arcana, and above the illustration on each card is an aphorism that heralds the luck of the draw. Naturally, the first thing I did when I opened my deck was find the DEATH card. On it, a frog-faced skeleton reclined on a beach chair eats a slice of watermelon beneath a pastel azure sky. "Live as cool as you like, you leave in a car with curtains," reads the card. Another one, JUDGEMENT, featuring a praying mantis striking a gavel against a sound block, reads: "By the time you've been judged guilty, you've learnt enough about the system to take the moral sting out of it." In this snapshot of nonsense literature (yet another operative genre), Aylett returns to the Kafkaesque. A preoccupation with absurdist bureaucracy, moral indoctrination, and the malevolent vicissitudes of the "Law" recurs in his fiction, as does an aphoristic dexterity that's downright rancorous in its ubiquity as much as its acuity.

Aylett's literature evokes a wealth of emotions. For every laugh it delivers, for example, there's usually an accompanying insight (a *Tao*) if not a hammer of erudition, and the aphoristic texture of the prose often drops both of these anchors at once. It's almost as if aphorisms control the author (a *Jinx*) allowing him to shirk the weight of their reconnaissance, then reeling him back in to *speak* their divinely comedic, meta-philosophical *fight*. The literature is Zarathustrian in this respect and riffs on the same muse as Nietzsche, who, in that pathological masterwork *Ecce Homo* (1908), admits: "My genius is in my nostrils" (96). So, too, does Aylett the Übermensch sniff out unseen truths and, like that pathological jackanape Jeff Lint, "unearth the bruises underground" (198).

This new, expanded edition of *Tao Te Jinx* collects aphorisms from the Aylett megatext as it currently stands, pushing daisies from *The Crime Studio* to *Hyperthick*—nearly three decades worth of material. It will be the fourth edition after Scar Garden Media's releases in 2004, 2006, and 2010. Complementing the many words of wisdom, hilarity, and darkness that span these pages are quotations and one-liners from the various Shakespearean clowns and sophists, parasites and villains, spastics and milquetoasts that populate Aylett's rich multiverse. As with earlier editions, here you will find a "manual to the trickster's Way of Confoundingly Honest Resentment" that's as good for a guffaw as it is for expanding your lexicon and reflecting on the (d)evolving condition of the Human Stain.

I was 28 when I discovered Aylett and my first story appeared in *Liquid Fiction*. I'm 51 now. In the last 23 years, I've published upwards of 1,000 stories, essays, reviews, and plays alongside over thirty books, including fiction, nonfiction, everything in between, and everything beyond the perimeter. Say whatever you want about my writing—nobody outworks me. *Nobody*. I won't allow it. I read and write all day and night long, taking breaks primarily to eat, lift weights, and be with my daughters. I don't care about anything else, and when I'm not reading and writing, I'm thinking about literature and art. Getting drunk used to be a pastime. Booze was the only thing that could switch off my hyperactive brain. I quit that years ago. I'm far from perfect, but I know myself. I know what I am, and I know the traumatic embers that enflame my work ethic, compelling me to pursue artistic expression and originality at every turn without compromise. Inevitably, sometimes my sense of self blows out of proportion. I think I'm better than I am. I think I'm special, like I did at the beginning of my career. I think I'm more than just another fleshbag who will live and die and be forgotten.

Then I remember the Tao of Aylett. I can read until my eyes roll into my skull and write until the phalanges pierce the skin of my fingers. Try as I might, I'll never achieve that level of artistic awareness and virtuosity. It makes me happy. It gives me comfort. The Tao will always be there, daring me to be better than I can be.

—Dreamfield, Ohio 2022

Bibliography

Aylett, Steve. *And Your Point Is? Scorn and Meaning in Jeff Lint's Fiction*. Raw Dog Screaming Press, 2006.

———. *Heart of the Original*. Unbound, 2015.

———. *Lint*. Thunder's Mouth Press, 2005.

———. *Novahead*. Scar Garden Media, 2011.

———. *Slaughtermatic*. Four Walls Eight Windows, 1997.

———. *Tao Te Jinx*. Third Edition. Scar Garden Media, 2010.

———. *The Aylett Tarot*. Scar Garden Press, 2022.

———. *Toxicology.* Four Walls Eight Windows, 1999.

Gibson, William. *Neuromancer*. Ace Books, 1984.

Lint, Jeff. *The Caterer* . Vol. 1, No. 3. September 1975.

Lyotard, Jean François. *The Postmodern Condition: A Report on Knowledge*. 1979. University of Minnesota Press, 1984.

McGowan, Todd. *The Impossible David Lynch*. Columbia University Press, 2007.

Nietzsche, Friedrich. *Ecce Homo*. 1908. Penguin Books, 1992.

Wilson, D. Harlan. "Goodbye, Beerlight." *Steve Aylett: A Critical Anthology*. Sein und Werden, 2016.

Hyperthick

Zigzagging to please is exhausting. —*Hyperthick*

cuboid coins the angels use and the collapsed melon he solemnly gave me one cold evening. This synopsis does no justice to the dreamlike quality of the episode. That night I looked out at the courtyard to see a pair of albino gill-men doing a sort of silent fandango. When I mentioned it the next morning he side-stepped the issue so fast he generated a small sonic boom. He packed ninety-one digressions into a three-minute conversation in which he was meant to be describing his chin. Leading the charge was claim that Jupiter's colloid.

"His confession was composed of randomly intersecting lines of jeopardy studded with dimes. Casual scrutiny suggested I was the Hydra's most boring head yet, living in a pressurized diving bell the color of brandy."

HYPERTHICK

THE COMPLETE
ACCOMPLICE

STEVE AYLETT

ONLY AN ALLIGATOR
THE VELOCITY GOSPEL
DUMMYLAND
KARLOFF'S CIRCUS

WITH AN INTRODUCTION BY
MICHAEL MOORCOCK

APHORISMS & QUOTATIONS

When someone tells you life's a dream, you can bet they're about to inconvenience you very badly.
—*The Complete Accomplice*

Government is like domestic abuse—it manages to make the victim feel guilty.
—*The Complete Accomplice*

How many times does a man have to shave before his chin gets the message?
—*Slaughtermatic*

The twists of tacking convention are pretty to some, not me.
—*Shamanspace*

Tough out the fake years and don't let the times waste your time.
—*Heart of the Original*

Try to accept that intelligence is aboard.
—*The Complete Accomplice*

The best way of getting into something is to think of it as mischief.
—*The Crime Studio*

Every atom's a golden ticket really. Ignite your chemistry and you can't get a slip of paper between you and paradise.
—*Hyperthick*

I discovered a means of exhilaration so obscure it was yet to be deemed illegal. The whole truth is a pleasure too intricate to be popular.
—*Novahead*

One afternoon I achieved a rate of seven hundred errors per second. I looked completely motionless like a hummingbird.
—*Hyperthick*

Finding a withered melon on the front step, Gregor gloomily considered his lifestyle.
—*The Complete Accomplice*

When I desire a spectacle I look to my own conscience.
—*Bigot Hall*

Most people approach the subject of suicide determined to be baffled.
—*Lint*

Painkillers are the drugs of the future.
—*Slaughtermatic*

When a monster passes, we take it for another whose favourable opinion we must seek.
—*The Complete Accomplice*

Man accepts diversity at every level of nature but his own mind. A million emotions; only two hundred words.
—*Bigot Hall*

If a memo burns faster than you can read it, nature is telling you something.
—*The Complete Accomplice*

In the soup but not of the soup.
—*Hyperthick*

Alfred Bork has called Lint's writing "pointillistic" and I think this derives from the fact that every single sentence comes directly at you. Each point is the head of a thread, a retrievable plumb-line of information. But few have taken up the option to draw on such threads.
—*And Your Point Is?*

It hurts so good to oppose fate.
—*The Nerve*

Do not hang a man and be surprised at his reaction.
—*Toxicology*

Any rate of resentment lags behind the situation.
—*The Complete Accomplice*

We have truth in order not to die of art.
—*Bigot Hall*

Lucifer is a black glove we wear to hide our own fingerprints.
—*The Complete Accomplice*

Civilisation is the agreement to have gaps between wars.
—*Lint*

Progress accelerates downhill.
—*The Complete Accomplice*

The tiresome idea that pain makes us feisty. I, for one, am simply exhausted.
—*Hyperthick*

Limited options crossing paths over and over can scratch a hole?
—*Hyperthick*

You've been suffocating tiny portions of yourself continually, a starry sky going out one by one.
—*Hyperthick*

One golfer a year is hit by lightning. This may be the only evidence we have of god's existence.
—*Atom*

"What's that thing when someone gets a knock on the head and suddenly can't remember anything about himself?"

"Death," said the barman, his face a mask of disapproval.
—*The Crime Studio*

Creative genius can crop up anywhere, even—though rarely—in the upper classes. The latter's abnormally high levels of criminality led to hopes of precocious inventiveness from that quarter, but nothing has happened. The well-to-do don't do much.
—*Heart of the Original*

Russia was never a communist country seeing as communism is the abolition of class, and all they ever did in Russia was abolish the middle one.
—*The Crime Studio*

Depends on your appetite. If you want the glass full, you perceive it as half empty; if you want it empty, you perceive it as half full. Some people settle.
—*The Nerve*

What happens when the hitcher and the driver are equally murderous?
—*Atom*

You're hanging into this society like an insect leg from a toad's mouth.
—*Novahead*

Crime is one of the many methods justice may select.
—*Slaughtermatic*

I'm not falling under the spell of your dodgy forgiveness.
—*Hyperthick*

It's hard for people to stampede when they're strutting.
—*Shamanspace*

Sid could tell with a doomed acceptance that this was the sort of over-familiar ghoul who'd think nothing of stabbing you with its chin.
—*The Complete Accomplice*

If only bluster was the force-field you imagine, eh?
—*Hyperthick*

All I have is a headache—but I would give it to you.
—*The Nerve*

Staring is its own reward.
—*Toxicology*

Live as cool as you like; you leave in a car with curtains.
—*Hyperthick*

Always call a bluff, for fireworks.
—*Hyperthick*

Eddie knelt and lifted a rock. "Lawyers," he whispered.
—*The Inflatable Volunteer*

The element of surprise is available to those who either appear suddenly or have always been there. Thus the shock on the gran's face when the ancient boulder fell.
—*The Inflatable Volunteer*

"The trick was to create social conditions in which a man is maimed and limited by his honesty," Krill explained.
—*Rebel at the End of Time*

My advice went in one nostril and out the other.
—*Hyperthick*

A cliché is like a womb—we can sleep there, hide there, be safe there. And like the womb it must be abandoned if we are to reach full adulthood.
—*The Complete Accomplice*

"Wouldn't we all shoot a mayor or two for a few laugh-lines?"
—*The Inflatable Volunteer*

In books there's nothing of the fish covered in the coldness of the sea, or the feeling of a star touching space. Bad for business.
—*The Inflatable Volunteer*

A sniper is like a genius—it's not enough to be one, you have to be one *at* something.
—*Slaughtermatic*

When the angel arrived it was with the burnt-dust smell of a bus.
—*Hyperthick*

If we got enough people spinning in their graves we could use it as a power source.
—*Heart of the Original*

"I've been selected to witness your blistering defeat at trial."

   "Aren't you defending me?"

   "Of course—I was using legal terminology."
—*The Complete Accomplice*

Honesty is the voice that is acceptable in every matter.
—*Shamanspace*

A sarcastic salute says a lot.
—*Hyperthick*

It's hard to determine, at the start, what you will be able to bear for a lifetime.
—*Lint*

A camel cannot be impressed.
—*The Complete Accomplice*

A shrapnel scar on my spine the colour of banana talks to me at night, filling the room with whispers.
—*The Complete Accomplice*

At the wedding they exchanged rings with such venom the priest let out a small cry.
—*The Complete Accomplice*

Your enslavement strengthens apace and escape lacks the spectacle you crave.
—*Hyperthick*

Part of enlightenment is knowing when you're being ripped off.
—*The Nerve*

For propaganda to resist erosion, calm voices must be seen as more absurd than hysterical ones.
—*The Complete Accomplice*

During sleep we do not work or consume, are not outward-looking, hysterical or entertaining, and are becoming healthier. Many would wish it abolished, in others.
—*Heart of the Original*

Oppression evolves, like everything else.
—*Toxicology*

Radio waves feel antique but they're far older.
—*Hyperthick*

"It is written here in our Constitution"—and the Mayor dabbled his fingers in a tray of water ...
—*The Complete Accomplice*

It's a telling tidemark for a nation when people have to do their own surgery.
—*Johnny Viable*

When someone starts saying "vestibule," you know you're in the wrong place.
—*The Complete Accomplice*

Saturn in Gemini in your second house leads to the confiscation of illegal earnings, which is how you could afford the second house in the first place.
—*Toxicology*

"Snail, Sarge?"
   "Don't mind if I do. What are they?"
   "Snails Sarge."
   "Snails. Don't mind if I do."
   "Get your face round that then."
   "What is it."
   "A snail, Sarge."
   "Snail. Alright then. Eat it do I?"
   "Eat it, Sarge. That's right."
   "What is it."
   "Snail—a snail, Sarge."
   "Snail."
   "A snail, Sarge. See? It's a snail."
   "Snail is it. Well now."
   "Snail."
   "Snail, eh. Well, don't mind if I do."
   "Good on yuh."
   "Right."
   "You eatin' it then?"

"Eh?"
"You eatin' that?"
"What is it."
"Snail, Sarge."
—*The Complete Accomplice*

One thing you'll say for skeletons, they'll always give you a smile.
—*Slaughtermatic*

From baptism font to wrist-bloodied basin.
—*The Inflatable Volunteer*

A good leg will know when to kick, know when to run, and handle the transition quickly.
—*The Complete Accomplice*

Economic slavery is a blade so sharp it takes years to realise you've been cut.
—*Rebel at the End of Time*

A wound is a smile saying, "You see, I was right about this place."
—*Hyperthick*

Fractal litigation, whereby the flapping of a butterfly's wings on one side of the world results in a massive compensation claim on the other.
—*Slaughtermatic*

Reform changes the shape of injustice.
—*The Complete Accomplice*

Regret is a rope at the other end of which is a younger version of you, all full of beans and acting like a moron.
—*Smithereens*

Parker always felt things in his bones because, he said, it saved space.
—*The Crime Studio*

The acknowledgement of fact. It becomes a little ritual in secret.
—*Hyperthick*

For many, school is an experience of such toxicity and destructiveness that it is merely a thing to spend the rest of their lives recovering from. It serves as aversion therapy or a system of encapsulated samples introduced to stimulate antibodies against creativity or knowledge.
—*Heart of the Original*

A shelter of immense preoccupation keeps off reality. On the cusp of learning, you know humanity is about to be blindsided by celebrity again.
—*Lint*

Max Gaffer made a rambling, convoluted remark about the Mayor's Picasso morality, by which his morals were crowded on to one side of his face.
—*The Complete Accomplice*

Dive into the waters of majority, see if you get clean.
—*The Complete Accomplice*

Coincidence conducts electricity. But it's not meant to.
—*Hyperthick*

Bad law is a boring dare.
—*Hyperthick*

The mind is horribly willing to resign before its time.
—*Smithereens*

Your bought world is losing value.
—*Hyperthick*

Lint created a text that was unsettling only to those who are unaware enough to be "settled" in the midst of the world's nightmare.
—*And Your Point Is?*

Pause any country and you'll spot subliminal torture in the frame.
—*Shamanspace*

Do you still dream of being praised by halfwits?
—*Hyperthick*

Infinity has so much structure it has no structure.
—*The Complete Accomplice*

Darkplan wars—success when nobody returns.
—*The Inflatable Volunteer*

I reckon I'll dismantle a crawdad and reassemble it in the likeness of a bishop.
—*Hyperthick*

Another room was given over to a grand mural of an eagle gliding through a canyon, which a plaque explained was symbolic of fascism moving through the democratic process.
—*Novahead*

There was a time when the extension of illegality to innocent acts could be used to manipulate men. But when guilt is no longer felt over acts of genuine criminality, what hope of instilling guilt in the innocent?
—*Slaughtermatic*

Those instants of pinpoint eternity and straining ecstasies leave a fellow enlightened to within an inch of his life.
—*Hyperthick*

Reality is the thing that doesn't need to be asserted.
—*Lint*

To see what is actually there it's useful to blindfold your language and look with your eyes.
—*Hyperthick*

They certainly were docile—such enthusiasm!
—*Hyperthick*

"Blundered in here with a stolen nest in one hand and a roulette wheel in the other."
—*The Complete Accomplice*

If you tape the average man's mouth shut he'll lie through his nose.
—*Smithereens*

When a man can't stop lying it ends up making a sort of sense despite him, an assemblage whose design gives him away.
—*Hyperthick*

Grandeur only works at low speed.
—*Toxicology*

Remnants of a cancelled timeline are always compelling in a lumpy way— airships, flying boats, the North American camel.
—*Hyperthick*

The people's thirst for propaganda was insatiable—we couldn't alarm them fast enough. I wondered if they knew something we didn't.
—*Johnny Viable*

Yield to doubt and glimpse a world of possibilities.
—*The Complete Accomplice*

He wanted to kneel and lick upward until his face was buried in her fur.
—*The Complete Accomplice*

It is a practice of mine never to punch a man whose face is redder on the outside than mine is on the inside
—*The Crime Studio*

I'd stood pickled in others' precepts for years. Before anyone could stop

me I developed an interest in honesty, a disease you can only catch from your own reflection.
—*Hyperthick*

The need to convince is unique to plain men.
—*The Complete Accomplice*

Running battles with the police allowed me to express my "cheeky" side.
—*Hyperthick*

Part of the cosmos is pure moxie!
—*Hyperthick*

History is buried alive.
—*The Complete Accomplice*

Things are as bad as our short time alive will allow.
—*The Complete Accomplice*

Specter was used to stating his opinions as law, a practice known as "Dworking."
—*Slaughtermatic*

A human being is more than a slotted head and churning legs, Mr. Banger.
—*Hyperthick*

His implied claim to at least one of the attributes of god was endorsed the first time he punished an innocent man.
—*Novahead*

He's as subtle as a harpist punching a horse.
—*Hyperthick*

I became preoccupied with the geometry of the world without me and its similarity to the world in which I was contained.
—*Hyperthick*

Jeff Lint's interpretation of Kafka's *The Trial* was that the guilt felt by K.—and depended upon by the state—derives from his having allowed the state to become so powerful in the first place. K. therefore ultimately accepts his punishment. In Lint's story "The Retrial," K. feels no such guilt because he allows no such influence and storms into every circumstance like a berserk Touretter, somehow spanning the most chasmic beartraps by sheer velocity of mischief.
—And Your Point Is?

A book can bite you like a snake or unhook its jaw to digest you whole, slowly. It may be a rosebud clutched around a compressed infinity, an engine with all the scintillatory operation of a Tibetan thangka or a blessing from around ten corners in someone else's breakdown.
—Heart of the Original

In the face of moral teachings many people offset their murders by paying a potential murderer to keep his urges in check.
—Novahead

The most amusing thing about a pantomime horse is having to shoot it twice.
—Bigot Hall

Sewn into myself, I'm screaming.
—Hyperthick

There's no satisfaction in blaspheming against something you don't believe.
—The Caterer

Space is limitless—manipulation therefore is limitless.
—The Complete Accomplice

He went off on tangents so extended they met the tangents of Martians coming the other way.
—Slaughtermatic

Pain is god trying to be funny. That's how out-of-touch It is.
—*Lint*

Insanity happens when all your adjustments to the world meet up by accident.
—*The Complete Accomplice*

Then the waiter came in, pink as a marzipan monastery.
—*Hyperthick*

"Let the record show that the defendant has given a greatly accelerated impersonation of a giraffe."
—*The Complete Accomplice*

A cynic is someone who finds out at birth what others find out at death.
—*The Caterer*

Exile is relief disguised as penance.
—*Lint*

Albatross for dinner. Bad omen.
—*Smithereens*

Consequences always look inevitable in retrospect, and usually ahead of time too, as the same facts are available in both cases.
—*Heart of the Original*

I've always been marginal, me.
—*The Inflatable Volunteer*

Life's bounty turns out to be French toast and trace amounts of puffin.
—*Hyperthick*

Spindly crutches descend upon the stairs, an insect bigger than you can handle.
—*Lint*

A crime archaeologist recently excavated a heist preserved in the Pompeii lava flow. The crook is aiming a spear at a shopkeeper, who is loading loaves into a bag. The shopkeeper's expression is no less or more surprised than those of today in similar circumstances.
—*Slaughtermatic*

You'll no longer have conversations, but merely dock declarations with others.
—*Hyperthick*

Why are we carrying on like this when the hot twilight air is full of flies? Why not lean on the pasture bars and watch it all? Bumble bees the size of dogs. These are our treacle days. And it's all nice and legal.
—*The Complete Accomplice*

Cars with portholes are cool.
—*Novahead*

There's no such thing as a normal angel. It's never done that way.
—*Atom*

A man without error is a geographical impossibility.
—*The Complete Accomplice*

Innocence. The favorite toy you can't believe you forgot.
—*Hyperthick*

Freedom in cyberspace'd be fine and dandy if we happened to live there.
—*Slaughtermatic*

Facts are acknowledged only when the events they relate to are far in the past and safely irrelevant.
—*Smithereens*

If the devil existed, it would be in the form of a crowd.
—*Heart of the Original*

Humanity can begin a season in the abstract and end it with blood in the roads.
—*The Complete Accomplice*

Take, sympathise, control. But the middle one has become a luxury. It gives nothing back.
—*Novahead*

In life a kind of justice pursued her, growing wings on her honesty. And wings, like honesty, are not socially comfortable.
—*Heart of the Original*

"What's worse—that the state abuses us specifically and by name, or that they abuse us while not acknowledging us specifically? Take time to think, Amy."

"The latter is more insulting, while perhaps allowing more leeway for escape?"
—*Johnny Viable*

There's no reason why inequality should be any less effective than individually contacted victims.
—*Heart of the Original*

If people truly don't return from the dead, then humanity is constantly passing out of the world, something is being lost—yet there are still bodies and bodies and bodies, moving and talking. Does this explain the increasing blandness, the diminishing thought, the dead eyes? What is passing out of the world, and not returning, is spirit.
—*Smithereens*

Let us forget the past—this is the only way to be genuinely surprised.
—*Slaughtermatic*

If you drink a glass of water while falling off a cliff it has the same effect as poison.
—*Hyperthick*

Thrown stones were once stars.
—*Lint*

We are iterations between immensities—allotted a random jumble of
dimensions and left to it. It's quite natural we should toggle between
dismay and alarm. It's not all fun, as Kermit's nephew would have you
believe.
—*Hyperthick*

Always eat a fish headfirst. You never know.
—*The Complete Accomplice*

It was difficult to tell where one bastard ended and another began.
—*The Crime Studio*

Thuds from a grave: a good thing?
—*And Your Point Is?*

Nuns would run shrieking, but as far as I can tell that's all they're for.
—*The Inflatable Volunteer*

Antonin Artaud had a face like a wet kestrel and more worries than a
shaved lion in a rental car.
—*Heart of the Original*

Authority takes everything. It nails the puddle of wine to the table.
—*Atom*

A society will manufacture an image of progress and locate it in the
direction it wishes to take us.
—*Shamanspace*

By living in a weighted sphere of honesty he is able to live unharassed,
as the orb is designed to seem quite uninteresting from the outside,
and unfashionable always from any angle.
—*And Your Point Is?*

People will do almost anything to avoid acknowledging that they're powerless. That's a sturdy handle.
—*The Complete Accomplice*

Write every story as if it was your last, whether suicide note or proof of life.
—*Heart of the Original*

When a man arrives with an elephant, he borrows the animal's majesty. And shrinks over long acquaintance.
—*Hyperthick*

I remember Chief Blince's remark about repaying my debt to society. I don't believe in revenge.
—*The Crime Studio*

The air was criss-crossed with a density of laws that could strip the skin off a man's head for a moment's inattention.
—*Novahead*

An unearthly shriek goes a long way.
—*Hyperthick*

Freedom yawns at rhetoric—its gaze wanders. The establishing of evil in such conditions will receive little attention.
—*The Caterer*

When someone gave him the white feather of cowardice he used it to smudge his aura.
—*The Complete Accomplice*

To him Marx and Rand were the same because he went by pant size.
—*Toxicology*

In queuing to end his life at least a thousand people were turned away.
—*The Complete Accomplice*

I won't be lectured to by someone whose nose is the same colour as his eyes.
—*Toxicology*

"At that time I will set upon a policy greatly at odds with your wellbeing, squashing your faces as though against a rippled pane of glass. This will be followed by a root and branch review, a clamour of ear-grinding excuses and, finally, the really backbreaking work of denying everything. One or two timid witnesses will drift down a river and deal out into the sea. Then I'll give a big horselaugh."
—*The Complete Accomplice*

In America, fundamentalist Christians claim the world was created 6,000 years ago. In Europe, people drink in bars that are older than that.
—*Heart of the Original*

A wound heals slower than a kiss.
—*Bigot Hall*

Nature is not murdered without a consequent haunting.
—*The Complete Accomplice*

Mankind mines a stratum of the obvious so thick it occupies a lifetime.
—*The Complete Accomplice*

"So you're from England? No room to move and a tax disk on your coffin. Poor kid."
—*Lint*

There is no more infernal amusement than the spectating of civilization's bind.
—*Slaughtermatic*

When every channel shows the same picture, you know it's something you should ignore.
—*The Complete Accomplice*

Hieronymus Bosch, whose idea of Paradise was a giant turkey baster surrounded by baffled wildlife. The egg-on-legs in his Hell appears a cosy abode and would be looked on with envy by the millions without shelter today.
—*Heart of the Original*

Berringer joked that he was a wanted man and showed us a dagger, claiming that it was "the very one."
—*Smithereens*

Professor Traven emerged from the house, his failures trailing behind him like a dead parachute.
—*Novahead*

Strong rules don't bend but break.
—*The Crime Studio*

I crept in to find my father with pennies on his eyes—and looking closer I saw they were made of foil-covered chocolate. Of course I stole and ate them. Magical guilt? Tell me about it.
—*The Inflatable Volunteer*

My father was placed in the care of the soil and numerous bugs. I was astonished at the change which was accepted.
—*Hyperthick*

Don't expect sincerity from a man unless the tide's coming in on him.
—*The Complete Accomplice*

Truth is not an interruption. Facts are facts in this world. The hospital turns with the rest.
—*Hyperthick*

Witness the baleful charms of gravity upon a plummeting wretch as nature behaves like disaster's friend.
—*Novahead*

Immortal? I don't want to still be alive when they're stacking chairs.
—*The Complete Accomplice*

The notion of morphic resonance states that an idea or behaviour con-
ceived in one member of a species can then arise in others at a distance,
and it may be that the decision to ignore certain ideas and inventions is
transmitted in the same way.
—*Heart of the Original*

It's a fragile system in which a frog is an emergency.
—*Smithereens*

The great thing about being ignored is that you can speak the truth with
impunity.
—*Toxicology*

The stars aren't too distant to discuss, why this?
—*Hyperthick*

Fire is born old.
—*The Complete Accomplice*

You think being permitted is the same as being free?
—*Shamanspace*

Whispering is satisfactory only when it is heard.
—*The Complete Accomplice*

These fools can't get enough of it. If a genie gave them three wishes,
they would select pasta for all three.
—*The Complete Accomplice*

"You see, Juno, it's like this. You can't go wrong spending money on
death and murder. A lot of people have noticed it through the years ...
All we need is deceit, an enemy, and negligence."
—*The Complete Accomplice*

The young are too intent to be truly sinister.
—*Atom*

A hundred percent of marriages end in divorce, disappearance or death.
—*Toxicology*

Cuteness is powerful. A sloth opens its eyes and it's sayonara, kid.
—*Hyperthick*

You'd think gangsters are the one place you'd find certainty.
—*Hyperthick*

It's not rebellion if they just sold it to you.
—*Smithereens*

Kali with her many arms couldn't slap any sense into that one.
—*Hyperthick*

Caught by the mortals in old age, an angel scattered itself like leaves.
—*Shamanspace*

America's make-believe is more dangerous than its reality.
—*Lint*

Untended, questions grow wild.
—*The Complete Accomplice*

Murder's the taking of one man's life by another—war's the other way around.
—*Slaughtermatic*

A man who can't be changed has no need to fight.
—*The Complete Accomplice*

If he was enthusiastic he hid it well.
—*Hyperthick*

The average legislator is driven by the desire to cool his molten igno-rance into some lasting obstacle.
—*Slaughtermatic*

Until the very last moment I entertained the possibility of being pleas-ant. Then he entered the room skidding on his belly like a puffin.
—*Hyperthick*

Prancer was trying to step with both legs at once and straining with hilarity at his experiment.
—*The Complete Accomplice*

"You joined this species by the seat of your pants."
—*The Crime Studio*

Suffice it to say I suddenly seraphized, waking to find the room burnt to rough gold and the carpet gone. All that's left are gemstones pulsing like bird hearts and buckled bike spangles in frozen tar. See attached invoice.
—*Hyperthick*

Like a cyclist, the critic is assuming you'll get out of the way.
—*The Complete Accomplice*

A crime doesn't have its being outside the law—the law has its being inside a crime.
—*Slaughtermatic*

"The darkest hour's just before the dawn."
   "So are the majority of bed deaths, Father."
—*Bigot Hall*

"Do you have nothing to say about your behaviour?"
   "Well, I'd rather not be doing it surrounded by spooked failures, but other than that ..."
—*Smithereens*

You can't argue with motive, my friend. If someone doesn't want to know something, you can't make them see it.
—*The Nerve*

The cops stood expecting our amusement to be paralysed in deference. Many had confused their profession with full human identity. I thought a few had guns, and asked someone why.

"To assure us that nice people carry guns too."
—*Toxicology*

The soul leaves the body out of flat disinterest.
—*Hyperthick*

He had long been curious at leaders' intermittent calls for a return to past values and had tested the notion by trying to build a house from the sky downwards.
—*Bigot Hall*

Originality irritates so obscurely that people may have to evolve to scratch it.
—*Shamanspace*

For the Lint hero, unlike the heroes of ancient myth, the unavoidable confrontation with his own nature occurs at the beginning or before the story starts, and he is first discovered sitting on the burning shell of a car, wearing some sort of seaweed bonnet and playing a lute. Even the mimsy and ineffective Alan Jay is first seen riding a tiger shark up an embankment and doing a double forward-flip into a barbecue to which he was not invited.
—*And Your Point Is?*

To be so hen-hearted? To live his life as stock footage? To guard forever against divergence into originality? To what end? And what would be left to him? By comparison his life of stress and concern thus far seemed a funky adventure.
—*Toxicology*

Can anyone corroborate your outburst?
—*Hyperthick*

Brank loved how much people hated his adolescent doorframe sermonising and so did a lot of other people.
—*Smithereens*

The few traffic lights in Accomplice changed with the seasons, beginning green in summer, then through yellow to a lovely russet red in the autumn when, like fallen leaves, they could be ignored.
—*The Complete Accomplice*

And he ran out with a spraycan, writing MY ARM IS AT AN ANGLE on a high wall.
—*Smithereens*

Oh my romantic dream of a certain arrangement of words and images that will trigger the universe! But the universe triggered long ago, blindsiding conservatives.
—*Hyperthick*

Laughter is the second name of truth.
—*Hyperthick*

Impervious to popularity.
—*SteveAylett.com*

When a man drops his wife's dish, the universe opens for a moment like a lion's jaws.
—*Toxicology*

A thing done despite absolutely everything is a wonder indeed.
—*Heart of the Original*

The media, poised to praise him after his death, sprang in with lamentations that he had been tragically neglected by commercial enterprise

and that it was baffling that his artistic genius had not been more appreciated. Their bitter embarrassment upon learning that he was still alive and open to their patronage drove a bigger wedge than ever between the media and Lint—they had no recourse but to pretend he did not exist at all.
—*Lint*

Do you think the past is contained within the present? The past has escaped to its own freedom and doesn't think of us.
—*The Complete Accomplice*

"I'm delighted by barnacles, I confess. Some people think they're the collars of special goblins. What do you say?"
   "I say a cleansing fire cannot come soon enough."
—*Hyperthick*

Biting enemies seems to be acceptable in a surprisingly narrow range of circumstances, or so a ninja shouted at me once.
—*The Inflatable Volunteer*

An obscure joy is available in those moments when the demands of authority are most at odds with those of our own wellbeing.
—*Hyperthick*

Vampire bat: cute, pig-faced bird which drinks blood. The family *Megadermitidae* cannot drink blood and are called "false vampires." Which goes to show that if you're a bat, you can't win.
—*Toxicology*

He looked up at me with a ruddy face, a nose which contained his brain and a smile which contained my fist.
—*Bigot Hall*

Fashion absurdities made of plastic will rock on the silt floor in a million years, meaningless in the dark.
—*Hyperthick*

We've been screaming so long we've started to harmonize.
—*Hyperthick*

The truth is never wrong.
—*Lint*

Gregor approached his betterment like a clown talking through a taut door chain.
—*The Complete Accomplice*

Each sneeze frees a hundred lawyers.
—*Toxicology*

By tradition those who make pacts with the devil have some success in life, so Stalkeye assumed he'd made a pact with god.
—*The Crime Studio*

"Time is not what people believe it is. It is the colour which is always present but which cannot be seen until truthfully named. Its name is not 'time.'"
—*Fain the Sorcerer*

Nobody dared waste time telling him we planned to ignore the order—every time he raised his face we tensed for the euphoria of disobedience.
—*The Inflatable Volunteer*

Sandwiched between every day is a page for notes, and starlight.
—*Hyperthick*

Truth, existing everywhere, can attack from any point—even from within your own body.
—*And Your Point Is?*

Leaping into an empty pram amid the screams of women, Eddie tried to reclaim his youth.
—*The Inflatable Volunteer*

She made him feel like a bomb disposal expert.
—*The Complete Accomplice*

God, the way man planned him, fell short of a diverse universe.
—*Hyperthick*

Nice day—sunny outside and I hadn't bled much.
—*Toxicology*

Sacrifice has been redefined as the harm, inconvenience, or death of others.
—*The Caterer*

And nobody say "Voilà" when you pull your gun out, for god's sake.
—*Hyperthick*

There should be a procedure to formally quit a species.
—*Novahead*

Failing through a funnel? Accompanied everywhere by a burning skull only you can see?
—*Hyperthick*

Those who match nothing but themselves rarely notice the hairpin turns of external decree. They think in the rich syntax that results from living life in the wrong order.
—*Heart of the Original*

For some the trance doesn't take and they are left to experience life eyes-open as though awake during an operation.
—*Hyperthick*

When a culture which is flat out on the floor insists on looking down as though from a progressive height, its perceptions are reduced almost to zero.
—*The Nerve*

I told her about the hard-scrabble cannibalism and systematic avoidance at large. Most potential tech had died by humanity's shortfall, as people found themselves less and less concerned with artificial longevity and neural interfacing, and more concerned with finding something—any-thing—to eat.
—*Novahead*

Chains live without air.
—*Shamanspace*

We have only a short time out of the dirt, then whammo!
—*Hyperthick*

Life is a moment to respond before we are repaid into the unknown.
—*Heart of the Original*

One of history's most notorious criminals, I also have a beautiful singing voice.
—*Hyperthick*

I was transfixed by a vista of interlocking errors, abiding in the sheer scale of it by limiting my attention to a local configuration.
—*Hyperthick*

Good old Minotaur. Airlock eyes and a brain of steel wool. Sectioned tail like an armadillo's. A class fiend for your money.
—*The Inflatable Volunteer*

During this time I adopted several views created by others, a deception that still shames me.
—*Hyperthick*

I'm not convinced the balance is right. Every moment of grace is paid for with eight months lost in a malarial swamp dressed only in a woollen bonnet.
—*Hyperthick*

Wisdom never comes of approval.
—*Fain the Sorcerer*

Oh to be in England in the cruellest month.
—*Toxicology*

"When the victim is ready, the bastard appears."
—*Novahead*

Lack imagination? Why not be a lackey?
—*The Complete Accomplice*

Then he banged open like a bad rocket. Accelerated backward into his own vanishing point, taking half the room with him. The silent implosion sucked furniture out of the visual first, then a glittering wind whooshed into the vacuum. I'm telling you he etherically decompressed in here.
—*Hyperthick*

When you fake a threat you grant options to trouble.
—*The Complete Accomplice*

Because I'd studied meditation I knew how to slow my heart almost to a stop, simply by imagining I was married.
—*Lord Pin*

I tried to bypass scrutiny by doing nothing. But no-one else was doing anything either.
—*Hyperthick*

En-masse humanity's not-so-secret desire to be robotic and dispense with the complication of variety or the need to consider others has resulted in a culture in which psychopathology is the appropriate mindset.
—*Heart of the Original*

The inhabitants of heaven and hell are political prisoners.
—*Shamanspace*

Catalytic satire may expend no energy while unlocking it in the space it occupies. At its best its very existence and placement is a confounding artefact which sends everything around it into silence and absurd defence. In this it resembles large portions of nature, the implications of which must be ignored if a person is to engage in society.
—*Heart of the Original*

Admiration can be informative and useful but awe shuts down creativity in a stunned white-out.
—*Heart of the Original*

Nothing to hide on either side, nothing to fear.
—*Heart of the Original*

An analyst pocketed my laments for eight years. Then he ran a hot-rod off a cliff and sniggered all the way down, dumbfounding the police. Later I discovered he'd been cataloguing my mistakes quite scrupulously, using a system of tin skulls that rang like bicycle bells.
—*Hyperthick*

Lint compared the internet to pulps such as *Weird Tales*—that magazine was now all but lost to decay, releasing the scent of cinnamon and sandalwood, and he wondered what would become of thoughts, correspondence and stories dependent upon continual support and electric current. He factored this into his legacy when, referring to Shelley's *Ozymandias* and seeming to forebode events after his death, he remarked that he had always found it overly optimistic to expect the two towers to remain standing.
—*Lint*

Scandal bores because it requires a foundation of consensus.
—*Heart of the Original*

Lint shows us the complete lack of paradox in modern life which is evident if we look at it honestly and with an acceptance of its detail.
—*And Your Point Is?*

The day maggots sing
I will join the army
I will join the army
The day maggots sing
When they do, call me
Maybe they swing
I will join the army
The day maggots sing.
—*Lint*

As long as you don't break, you can be used.
—*Hyperthick*

Like any valuable commodity, the most dangerous time for an idea or philosophy is during transfer.
—*Heart of the Original*

Pity the spectators of revolution ... its success is not their success, and nor is its failure.
—*The Complete Accomplice*

If you want to live your life as prologue, take orders.
—*The Caterer*

No idea is so great that people won't quickly set about turning its gold into lead.
—*Hyperthick*

He was trying to look proud but didn't really know anything about it.
—*The Complete Accomplice*

Above her bed, the dreamcatcher burst into flames.
—*Rebel at the End of Time*

Duty enhances the handsome man, is an added burden to the unloved.
—*The Complete Accomplice*

Those who know do not speak, those who speak do not know. Thus wisdom remains uninherited.
—*Toxicology*

A human, a creature issued with a heart like a fatty frog, bone shoes, a skull to keep the rain off and death as standard.
—*Hyperthick*

Obedience built in layers will not be fragile.
—*Johnny Viable*

Manage them right and they'll rebel about the wrong things, if at all.
—*The Nerve*

Do they find fashion and obedience voluptuous or just blunder into it? Uncanny how the dazed all look alike. There's an angry certainty.
—*Hyperthick*

"Deceived and integrated"—put that on my headstone.
—*Hyperthick*

Disgrace is one of the classics, requiring a great number of players.
—*The Complete Accomplice*

No-one entirely succeeds in getting bent back into shape.
—*Heart of the Original*

Educated perhaps in the terrifying arts, the barman was silent.
—*The Inflatable Volunteer*

"You look like a wishbone in a coat."
—*Novahead*

Edgy was a practitioner of fridge meditation, that moment of blank reverie which occurs upon opening the fridge and forgetting why.
—*The Complete Accomplice*

And in the same moment, the opposite flavor like a secret.
—*Hyperthick*

The puppet Pantanal cuts his own strings, knowing that it means true death. When matter becomes so trapped by portrayal, it's agony.
—*Hyperthick*

In regard to bad reviews he said, "Hopefully such expressions of disapproval are stages in the journey toward being cut loose entirely."
—*Lint*

A tired despot tries to dominate the already imprisoned by superimposed re-enactment and the more he pyramids himself in the same position he becomes immobile, dependent, vulnerable.
—*Johnny Viable*

Last time I was here you mentioned an idea so fabulously deep and terrifying I woke up with a smashed pelvis and a tattoo of Stan bloody Laurel. Watcha readin'?
—*Hyperthick*

The tip of his long downcurving nose having fused with his upturned chin, Noam B Turbot had reached the age of realising there was no reward. Hair grew from his eyes. There was a good angel on one shoulder and a bad angel on the other, both drunk. He looked out the mossy window, mouth pursed like a fist. "It's as I suspected. The sun, rising at an angle, has inflicted another morning upon us all." He shook his head dismally.
—*The Complete Accomplice*

O'Nolan was a cast-iron genius and master of the Irish art of falling sideways into a sentence.
—*Heart of the Original*

"I'm fully capable of breaking my own nose, I hope."
—*Toxicology*

Extending the Warren Commission's flight of fancy, Lint theorizes that the Magic Bullet was a ricochet from that fired by John Wilkes Booth at Lincoln in 1865.
—*Lint*

Instantly thwarted upon deployment, some theories can survive only in a place where there are not any circumstances. Like a scale model, the theory does not behave like the real thing.
—*Heart of the Original*

The flipside to "cruelty before kindness" is the south London practice of smiling at a man you are about to push through a plate glass window.
—*Heart of the Original*

What can you say about someone who entered heaven like a bird through a jet engine?
—*Hyperthick*

Gun stripping is the tea ceremony of America.
—*Toxicology*

Curiosity is honest or it is inoperative.
—*Novahead*

At times humankind has been a paragon of common sense. Steaming jungles hide the traces presumably.
—*Hyperthick*

Truths snow into a lake, dissolving and lost.
—*Toxicology*

I thought things couldn't get any worse—that's how young I was.
—*The Inflatable Volunteer*

Concrete cannot complete the universe.
—*Smithereens*

The Japanese will hand you a business card with both hands; the British will propel you under a train the same way.
—*Lint*

I had to build up a composite image from the times he ran past the door.
—*Hyperthick*

The crux of a matter is very small, and easily missed.
—*Hyperthick*

The geometry of religions is interesting. Along certain vectors they can be placed over each other with no overhang and no template discrepancy.
—*Novahead*

When do you know finally that a secret's successful?
—*Shamanspace*

No-one wants a nuanced cavalry do they?
—*Hyperthick*

Under our lives death continues like the blank tape under a recording.
—*Toxicology*

Art is one of those sure scapegoats, absorbing all consequence with only mild surprise.
—*Lint*

Luckily for the book trade, most writers haven't enough passion to ever burn out.
—*Heart of the Original*

Real creativity is a ferocity of consciousness.
—*Heart of the Original*

Toward the end all the cities bunched together as if for reassurance.
—*Hyperthick*

When life's bruise goes all the way through, everything changes colour.
—*Hyperthick*

Recoil is like hearing your own accent.
—*Novahead*

Some writing is less intent on what it says than on where your mind has to manoeuvre itself to understand it. Once in that place, forget the text and look around.
—*Heart of the Original*

Everyone reckons spirits are a right laugh to flurry and snort over the houses—don't you believe it.
—*The Inflatable Volunteer*

"They say life begins at forty."
  "On the contrary, sir, it begins where it ends—at nought."
—*Toxicology*

I have never seen a scorpion shrug—I have never seen a government err to the good.
—*The Complete Accomplice*

Defenders of the Bible claim there are no accounts of Jesus's teachings in the forty days after his resurrection because he couldn't stop laughing.
—*Heart of the Original*

"Plenty more fish in the sea," Gregor hummed, "and they all hate me."
—*The Complete Accomplice*

Those chilling words: "It's all been arranged."
—*Hyperthick*

I was bored. Believing she could have no idea why, I explained it in finely crafted detail, after which I was astonished to see her anger increase.
—*Novahead*

He's got a medical bracelet that says: "Just throw me away."
—*The Complete Accomplice*

Books. In jewelled binding, oiled and polished like an antique gun, fattened by souls like a Chinese lantern ...
—*Hyperthick*

Those who mistake their religion or profession for full human identity are surprised when people treat them accordingly, though the benefit of the doubt is often granted. Many otherwise sensible people anthropomorphise the police.
—*Heart of the Original*

Unnoticed by the target, the strongest dislike goes into thin air.
—*The Complete Accomplice*

By the time you've been judged guilty, you've learnt enough about the system to take the moral sting out of it.
—*The Complete Accomplice*

Certain ceremonial masks of sub-Saharan Africa portray expressions of astonishment and provide relief from having to repeatedly fake surprise at the same things—an energy-saving bliss reserved for the tribal shaman.
—*Heart of the Original*

"Unless it's covered in gold," she said, pausing to drag on a cigarette, "it's worth no more than you are."
    "You mean if I was covered in gold I'd be worth something?"
    "I didn't say that."
—*Smithereens*

Context is everything. Take a dead, dry molecule from an orange, balance it on your finger—utterly useless to one and all. But put it in a box of granola, and it's gold dust.
—*Atom*

Marshall Hurk recalls: "He'd stand there tensing his stomach and say, 'Punch me—I can take anything.' Of course because of the false head we didn't know which of us he was talking to, so we all hit him at the same time. It was brutal."
—*Lint*

A dream falls asleep, fish staying under too long.
—*The Caterer*

"City" is short for "calamity."
—*Hyperthick*

London: a mistake built to last a thousand years.
—*Lint*

Some people keep their faces on the inside.
—*Atom*

Despair is not a subtle business.
—*The Complete Accomplice*

Videogames are meant to be an escape from the hassles of life but there too we are subjected to the violent stylings of vampires, cops and zombies.
—*Heart of the Original*

Bodies are street clothes of the spirit, a fattening wallet of things.
—*Toxicology*

An octopus has many arms, yes? And every bit of every arm is octopus, every inch. It's not bird or dog, right? Evil's the same. There's no real king or centre to it.
—*The Complete Accomplice*

I was born in a town so new it had only one mood.
—*Hyperthick*

The dog-in-a-sidecar joy experienced upon encountering even a single book which is active, that adds countless new elements to the literary periodic table, will swoon you into fizzing pools of rediscovered self-respect.
—*Heart of the Original*

Rasputin was dubbed the "mad monk" because, in times as conservative as our own, he sat down on one chair and rested his legs on another. He repeated this "two-chair jamboree" in several venues, and the practice was later thought to be the source of his mystical powers.
—*Heart of the Original*

Bob though—now there's a scary one. He'd drawn several dozen nerves out of his chin and deliberately tangled them to resemble an ordinary beard.
—*The Inflatable Volunteer*

Those who speak of the golden age of community overlook those ages when it was possible to be left alone.
—*Heart of the Original*

She was expelled from flesh, into flesh, and began to suspect how rare novelty would be.
—*Hyperthick*

Born surrounded, an ambush!
—*Hyperthick*

All dependence and renunciation go unrewarded in the universal jaws of experience.
—*Slaughtermatic*

Remember a few years ago, the nationalism and other state-sponsored insecurities? What I thought were marginal actions had a tyranny up and running within months.
—*Hyperthick*

Endurance has many benefits. I once crouched in a stinking marsh for three years.
—*Hyperthick*

The fear of the intensity that comes with real creativity, that house tornado in which intermeshing components roll and radiate in collisions of velocitous bliss, is a pretty good gauge of your final creation's power. Heaven is hard to be around.
—*Heart of the Original*

It takes patience to appreciate the wrong reply.
—*Atom*

And the angles on these dimensions, it's all pretend, like the gears on a bicycle.
—*Hyperthick*

Notice my prehensile nose? That's to speed up the grieving process.
—*Hyperthick*

Backbone needs a body.
—*The Complete Accomplice*

Justice is a different species than cause and effect.
—*Toxicology*

Voltaire exercised such unfashionable integrity of thought he threw the race into a sort of asymmetry.
—*Heart of the Original*

All you've done is undress the problem.
—*Hyperthick*

In Florida an old guy found he was treated with strange respect at a certain diner and would be left alone to dine gratis and for nothing so long as he accepted that everyone called him Joe. One day he went in

and was beaten to a pulp by the entire crowd. Months later he'd recovered enough to notice that the day before the incident, Joe DiMaggio had died.
—*Heart of the Original*

Since childhood I'd been suspected of imagination.
—*Slaughtermatic*

Freedom. They think it's a thing they can only lose by giving it away.
—*Hyperthick*

Point enough and people will look at you.
—*The Complete Accomplice*

A fixed stare better have a payoff or it's just boring, even in a cat.
—*Hyperthick*

The notion of innocence as a form of aggression against society.
—*Slaughtermatic*

"You've got to laugh otherwise you'll cry."
   "I see no impediment to doing both at once."
—*Bigot Hall*

At what time are people so reckless with meaning? When only the utterly powerful can risk an act of kindness.
—*Atom*

Ah, breathe that air, the best there is! Or else.
—*Hyperthick*

Drake led him through into a wizard's laboratory hung with triangular clocks, and explained the principles of building a diceheart. "Like many human beings, it owns three opinions and, by alternating these to the right timing, it can reproduce the external appearance of thought."
—*Fain the Sorcerer*

A gallery in the tomb was stacked with kestrels, each positioned in a different golfing stance. Even the facial expressions were varied.
—*Hyperthick*

Characters should be as special as Hindu gods, each the most intense at the time you are with them.
—*Heart of the Original*

Oh my brothers it's a fine thing when the most we can hope for is a kick upside the face from a saviour.
—*The Inflatable Volunteer*

Presenting yourself as an icon of resolve while in dreams you are chased by cattle.
—*Hyperthick*

I cottoned on to adversity at once. Too late I learned there was no way to measure it.
—*Hyperthick*

Their understanding's hamstrung by the notion that something's not serious if it's funny.
—*Hyperthick*

It's only good manners to wave to one's assassin.
—*The Complete Accomplice*

In politics, money and bones are what's left after the tide goes out.
—*Heart of the Original*

You implied this would be a cautionary tale. Yet it concludes with you eating a slap-up meal and wearing a golden bonnet.
—*Hyperthick*

Religion ruins angels.
—*Hyperthick*

Always of a serious disposition, I was also possessed of a resentment at having to grow while the world was losing its flavour.
—*Bigot Hall*

My father went over Niagara Falls in a barrel. Death hissed open like an automatic door.
—*Hyperthick*

Their inquiry was so relentlessly assumptive no information could move in their direction.
—*Hyperthick*

"To those with fully-functioning senses the planet Earth is already a living hell and to such folk the prohibitions of those who claim to be in authority come across as absurd at best, drowned out as they are by the high-frequency roar of hypocrisies too extreme to process. Most aware people dream of living a mere few instants of peace, away from the hysterical admonitions of neighbour, god and government. The sins listed are uninventive and boring, and the constant assumption that people are aching to commit them seems designed to insult the human imagination."
—*Smithereens*

A large expenditure of words for a modest incident involving a cursed doll and a fireball.
—*Hyperthick*

Those who profit from a problem mock workable solutions.
—*Hyperthick*

Zero-footprint architecture simultaneously provokes the accusation of outdated hippiedom and the protest that it is unprecedented.
—*Heart of the Original*

Everyone knows what's a *real* crime.
—*Atom*

Flags dress clowns.
—*Hyperthick*

At school I had trouble with geometry—parts of my body angled off into a dimension invisible from there. Recently I saw one of my child-hood arms emerging from the corner of a brownstone building, very briefly.
—Preface to *The Complete Accomplice*

Authority insists that misery is an education.
—*The Complete Accomplice*

I decided long ago that one should live as one's disastrous self, on the grounds of honesty.
—*The Complete Accomplice*

Anything said in a cross voice is funny.
—*Hyperthick*

"It'll make a man of you."
    "Which particular one?"
—*Johnny Viable*

Life and death have equal authority in nature. When laws contradict so fundamentally they cause mere confusion in the average soul.
—*Slaughtermatic*

It's only some facts that a name will stick to—others are too slippery, fast or fierce.
—*The Complete Accomplice*

The future is obvious.
—*Heart of the Original*

Human beings aren't content to cast reason aside. It has to hit someone.
—*Heart of the Original*

Lobsters live up to 50 years, each more sinister than the last ... On most days it lays in the murky depths like a discarded wrench, its specialized head crowded with antennae and old ideas ... The collective noun for lobsters is a "belter."
—*Hyperthick*

There's more to villainy than a helicopter deck and a propensity for violence.
—*Hyperthick*

The coelacanth, a dinosaur fish thought long extinct, became a media sensation when fishermen caught one in 1938. Known for its Clanger armour and merry smile, the coelacanth is now thought to bestow luck on those who catch it, especially those into whom it sinks its needle-like teeth. Yet what if it had never been thought obsolete? Sailors would probably kick it away with a bitter curse, calling it "the mudlark of the sea" or "Mary."
—*Heart of the Original*

He considered a career conducted at a velocity which, even if he blew apart, meant the end of the enterprise would be of adequate interest.
—*Lint*

Start your case from a position extrapolated way forward as if deliberately to annoy.
—*Heart of the Original*

You'll be re-extinguished on a daily basis.
—*Hyperthick*

It's a good thing it's true, because it's pretty ugly.
—*Heart of the Original*

Frown and you're using your best wares for something that truly expresses what you feel.
—*The Inflatable Volunteer*

Like legislation, superstition overlays generality with fine specifics.
—*Hyperthick*

His heart's a radio tuned between two stations.
—*The Caterer*

Activity is often wastefully over-wrought—for instance, only one small lesson can be learnt from an avalanche.
—*The Complete Accomplice*

The average life story is as graceless and practical as a scallop blurting its way along the seabed.
—*Hyperthick*

By the time I realised with horror that life was no mere passing fancy, I'd grown attached to its compensatory malices.
—*Novahead*

"You're basically a rocking horse with a human head."
—*Hyperthick*

"There are walls in people, sick and essential."
—*The Complete Accomplice*

A baying mob's the thing to prevent a man from making plans and thinking of the future.
—*The Complete Accomplice*

The law is where reality goes to die.
—*The Crime Studio*

Many people defer the achievement of anything interesting to their offspring. This postponement may roll over for a hundred generations before either they stop pretending or someone finally accomplishes something and is frozen out of the family for being a weirdo.
—*Heart of the Original*

A town like a missing tooth. Wind sucking thru alleys. Bandaged stores.
Factories plugged into the sky.
—*Hyperthick*

Deference, reverence or expected bafflement—these keep the content
unexplored.
—*Heart of the Original*

This is less a resume than a detailed settling of accounts.
—*Hyperthick*

He proceeded to demonstrate what he called "the sawmill essentials"
of persuasion with various expert shoves, workshop horrors and other
morale-blasting monkeyshines. It was like a sort of electric birthday,
and seemed designed to provoke me into a reckless and unguarded
outburst. I didn't think of many remarks, except the unvoiced one that
they didn't go nearly far enough. As it was I seemed to horrify them
every time I opened my mouth—even when I asked explicitly after the
relevant protocol.
—*Novahead*

Dumb as a trophy? Brain vanishingly small? Tempted to wear someone
else as a lucky charm?
—*Hyperthick*

I had big plans when I was your age, and look at me now, with edible
flanks and a chin like a dirty speedboat.
—*Hyperthick*

It's a good game to remain silent when someone wants to be inter-
rupted.
—*Heart of the Original*

Jeff Lint was told he wrote as if *Moby Dick* had never been published, to
which he responded that most people lived as if it hadn't.
—*Smithereens*

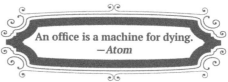

An office is a machine for dying.
—*Atom*

'Distressingly brilliant'
The Guardian

STEVE AYLETT

ONLY AN ALLIGATOR
Accomplice Book 1

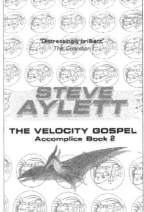

'Distressingly brilliant'
The Guardian

STEVE AYLETT

THE VELOCITY GOSPEL
Accomplice Book 2

Confusion hides its origins.
—*The Complete Accomplice*

A hugely impressive example of outrageous
literary wit.
STARBURST

STEVE AYLETT

DUMMYLAND

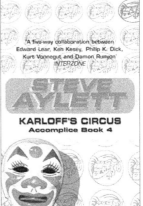

'A five-way collaboration between
Edward Lear, Ken Kesey, Philip K. Dick,
Kurt Vonnegut and Damon Runyon'
INTERZONE

STEVE AYLETT

KARLOFF'S CIRCUS
Accomplice Book 4

There may come a moment in a person's life when he finds that he has sampled finally all that is on life's menu—and upon considering the bill of fare, decides in all reason that it is a shabby, limited affair and not to his taste.
—*Fain the Sorcerer*

Reality is hard to caricature—it already goes over the line.
—*Novahead*

A riot of nature is the definition of a riot.
—*The Complete Accomplice*

"Nobody's free until everyone is, right?"
   "Until someone is."
—*Toxicology*

A ghost is the afterimage of someone not seen during their lifetime.
—*Hyperthick*

I approached the local chemist with the words "Pharmaceutical friend, we meet once again in the wrinkled throat of stacked odds" and that was the end of it.
—*The Inflatable Volunteer*

Regret is the broadest frontier.
—*Atom*

Real suffering is not a spectacle for philosophers—too messy.
—*The Complete Accomplice*

Debt's a dominance bite.
—*Hyperthick*

We try to live by the false boon of law's detail. Yet only nature's detail is infinite.
—*The Complete Accomplice*

A good deal of forbidden honesty has pointed to the fact that society is a temporary construction of dovetailed discrepancies. For the conscientious this results in a sadness so immense and informed that no rational mind can escape it.
—*Hyperthick*

Someone else's energy is like sliding down a bannister—it gets you there but then you have to think about it.
—*Hyperthick*

Corruption is only self-vanquished—thus corruption is not vanquished.
—*The Complete Accomplice*

"We may change; we may change a victim."
—*The Complete Accomplice*

The truth becomes an unattended sideshow.
—*The Complete Accomplice*

If all roads lead to Rome, how can anyone who lives there ever leave?
—*The Crime Studio*

Ah well, it's summer somewhere.
—*Hyperthick*

Justice knows when it's not wanted.
—*The Complete Accomplice*

Believing that he argues for his race, Drake tells Quine that laws and systems are "not personal." Quine replies: "Everything's personal, Drake. Everything that happens to a person."
—*And Your Point Is?*

If you're going to write, write something interesting and original, or get the fuck out of the way.
—*Smithereens*

Penguin: black and white creature with a bill, often mistaken for a lawyer.
—*Toxicology*

The universe does what it wants and takes its time. Meanwhile we've all the endurance of pastry.
—*Hyperthick*

People who've had a lot of good luck deny that luck exists—those who've had a lot of bad know it does.
—*Shamanspace*

Guilt's a debt in the head.
—*Atom*

"I survived my brush with that sandwich you made."
—*Hyperthick*

If music be the food of love, why haven't birds got ears?
—*The Crime Studio*

"Look at this bullet sir—the lifespan of an aphid, but by gad the changes it can wring."
—*Atom*

The great man carries a number of auxiliary morals of his own devising.
—*The Complete Accomplice*

Parables work something out in the privacy of another problem.
—*Heart of the Original*

Employment is atrophy speeded up.
—*Lint*

Under a rigor mortis sky lay an entire chunk of landmass so lacking in real mental sustenance it had surpassed blandness and gone into

reverse, denuded of refusal or examination, sap or invention! Nothingness repeated across the flavourless drifts of a trend desert! Epidemic technology and lack of independent imagination would keep things fast and hollow. It was really only a rather terminal version of the general way we avoid saying anything original or interesting because we know it upsets people.
—*Novahead*

He possessed the anonymity of those who are in such a state of health and standard opinion as to be almost undetectable to the human eye.
—*The Crime Studio*

Circus clowns have no accountability. They can do anything, no-one knows who they are, what they intend or what they mean by it all. We tolerate them only thru embarrassment. When will someone take a stand?
—*The Caterer*

Did you spot where Henry went wrong? He did over ninety-thousand dollars' worth of damage before he even left the house, a hectic fiasco which shattered every important bone in his body. Stay safe, kids!
—*Hyperthick*

Think thin—or better still, dead.
—*The Nerve*

A silent dot falls from one depth to another, muddling into the invisible. That's life.
—*Hyperthick*

Those who burst out thinking in public encounter not only sarcasm and physical aggression but a total lack of legal recourse.
—*Heart of the Original*

And when the pen priest told them the walls of hell were four thousand miles thick, they began at once to formulate a plan for breaking in.
—*The Crime Studio*

Dig thru a millionaire. More than gore?
—*Hyperthick*

The upper classes—so at home in a vacuum they can find three syllables in it.
—*The Complete Accomplice*

He gave two sighs—or maybe he was breathing.
—*The Complete Accomplice*

A clay pelvis makes for careful walkin'.
—*Hyperthick*

We're snakes created at one end and destroyed at the other.
—*Hyperthick*

Murder, theft, riot—they could not permit it to be true.
—*Slaughtermatic*

Life is quantum entanglement, a red labyrinth of delays and repeated perplexities.
—*Fain the Sorcerer*

At one point I hid in a collapsed section of a previous belief.
—*Hyperthick*

Never roast a farmer. If you think they complain under normal circumstances, you don't know the half of it.
—*Toxicology*

"Have you accepted Jesus as your personal saviour?"
   "Do I *look* like I have?"
—*Toxicology*

Toto read a newspaper article which estimated that crime was taking place at a rate of one crime every four seconds. Toto had always assumed

that crime was constant—like ten or twenty per second—and the revelation of these four-second pauses fired his curiosity. Why four seconds? Why intervals of no crime? Like a scientist who agitates atomic particles to observe their behaviour, Toto decided to study crime on a quantum level by creating wild fluctuations in its frequency.
—*The Crime Studio*

"I won't be here forever. I go on the record for the day you work it out."
—*The Complete Accomplice*

Used a replica gun to steal a replica sportscar and experienced a replica of remorse.
—*Slaughtermatic*

My hair was my conscience; I was glad when it went.
—*The Complete Accomplice*

Dreams always end before you kill the last person.
—*The Crime Studio*

A king is someone who fell into a chair.
—*The Promissory*

Folk say the gas chamber's just as cold-blooded as some homicides, but I think it's a crime of passion.
—*Toxicology*

The bastard planted a dead lizard one time, then while he was pretending to cry, he showed his arse to the whole world. That was a day for eyelids.
—*The Complete Accomplice*

Trouble's the only thing which can result from posing in a doorway with your trousers on only one leg. And it's the bare leg, not the trousered one, which will be the cause of that trouble.
—*The Inflatable Volunteer*

Nothing like a spider in the mouth to get you thinking.
—*The Inflatable Volunteer*

Money immediately provides a means of issuing unthinkable orders to good men.
—*Rebel at the End of Time*

Carlos Castaneda heard of the Aztec god Quetzalcoatl and mistakenly worshipped an axolotl, an antlered albino tadpole the size of a parsnip.
—*Heart of the Original*

Lint encouraged individual actors to perform different plays at the same time during performances, so that one actor would mount the stage to enact *Born With a Double Skull* while his fellow actor might be working from *Make a Wish Piranha* and another from *Slave Labor For Lovers*— their interaction more closely resembled the chaos of real life than anything he could have scripted.

"Many of you lost a darlin' during the war," states Jack at the start of *Blame the Mouth*, at which a patchwork donkey ran on shouting, "There are too many imbeciles in the bucket!," the opening line of *Certainly You Will*. Lint loved these random intersections, and the ill-lit gasps and dreadful conclusions of the audience thrilled him.
—*Lint*

A disaster is spilled truth.
—*Hyperthick*

"Will they reel in surprise at the next disaster Eddie or will they learn?"
   "I think they will reel in surprise."
—*The Inflatable Volunteer*

Only a fraction of history has been read into the record.
—*Hyperthick*

There was barely enough room to change his religion.
—*The Crime Studio*

I mentally repeated the local zenbit for clearing the mind: "Anything a potato is wrong about ..."
—*Novahead*

Snapper believed he could release his prejudices only by expressing them, and would believe this until he was buried in worms and clay.
—*Bigot Hall*

He said he didn't like my kind and I was filled with the delirious expectation that he would identify me as a common species—that there were others like myself. I controlled my excitement, but he seemed to sense it—his gaze wavered uncertainly.
—*The Crime Studio*

The cosmos was a bust. Had to change the rules to end it early.
—*Hyperthick*

All cities are designed for the same scenarios.
—*Lint*

The sticky infinity of unformed ideas is so rarely visited by humanity that many notions have assembled themselves in exasperation and crowded forward for easy access, free offers to attract the attention. Like brewers' fruit left so long on the branch that it begins to ferment itself, the merest touch brings them into your hand.
—*Heart of the Original*

Fiction isn't a threat to those who know the difference.
—*The Complete Accomplice*

Language will die of slow starvation.
—*The Complete Accomplice*

The active intelligence of a group doesn't settle around the level of the stupidest person in the group, but lower.
—*Heart of the Original*

There's no limit to what a dying system will demand of you.
—*Toxicology*

Even my compromises are in ruins.
—*Novahead*

Locked in an empty aircraft hangar he'd find a mistake to make.
—*Bigot Hall*

Those who lead double lives do so because they can only count that far.
—*Slaughtermatic*

Lacking adventure, and thus creating no stories. And because it creates no stories, it is a wisdom repeatedly lost and only by chance rediscovered. True wisdom is like that. Not spectacular.
—*Fain the Sorcerer*

The habit of thinking and recalling in their appliances rather than their own heads has left the greater proportion of the populace as empty, predictable and available as an arcade duck.
—*Smithereens*

Seemed she should learn to smile when she was unhappy, to stop laughing, to speak up, to never speak to strangers, to share guilt for the acts of strangers, that strangers made the laws of the land, that the laws of the land valued things over life, that life ended if a stranger decided it, to be where she could be found, to feel one thing and do another. How could she hang so many contradictions in one skull?
—*Toxicology*

Some fabulous religious memorabilia but it tends to get stolen. The test is whether you mind.
—*Hyperthick*

Thoreau's *Walden* is one big beautiful restraining order.
—*Heart of the Original*

Our ordinary measures of hypocrisy fail us before the operations of government and modern commerce.
—*Heart of the Original*

Much of people's mental energy goes into positioning themselves so that they can be surprised by results disastrous to others. It's a central component of the opt-out from consequence.
—*Rebel at the End of Time*

True creativity, the making of a thing which has *not* been in the world previously, is originality by definition.
—*Heart of the Original*

"Little do they know I've the morality of a jack-in-a-box!"
—*Hyperthick*

Nothing much interesting happens amid a conformity so innate it cannot clearly perceive or discuss itself.
—*Heart of the Original*

Is a gold bridge worth more than those who cross it? Is a stone bridge?
—*Hyperthick*

His bulk was the only thing standing between justice and chaos, and he had so far kept these conditions innocent of one another.
—*Slaughtermatic*

"Will you come to my party?"
    "I won't prevent it."
—*The Caterer*

Posh place. Windows on the ceiling. Carpet on the walls. Tiles on the floor.
—*Novahead*

A call to life given with such banal vigour it loses all meaning.
—*Hyperthick*

Cryptozoologists love telling the tale of the carny who stitched a blowfish and a bat together, only to find he had created a lawyer.
—*Heart of the Original*

Eddie gave a lecture to a bunch of school kids as to how his life had been wrecked by the simple inability to differentiate food from garbage. By delineating each of his mistakes he left a clear trail for them to follow if they wanted to be like him—sun-bronzed, respected and paid by the truckload to talk this crap at a public venue. Then he bit the head off a live hen and spat it at the front row, where the blank faces of the organisers received it like a sacrament.
—*The Inflatable Volunteer*

Mad chance gave us the Brautigan-like oddness of the Bible's camel-and-needle's-eye image, the result of the Aramaic word "gamla" meaning both "camel" and "rope."
—*Heart of the Original*

Denial. Vacuum competes with vacuum. Laws outlaw the harmless to make the effective inconceivable. Scholarly incomprehension. No questions asked. Banality given the terms and prestige of science. Ignorance worn like a heraldic crest. Mediocrity loudly rewarded. Misery by instalments. Hypocrisy too extreme to process. Maintenance of a feeble public imagination. Lavish access to useless data. Fashion as misdirection.
—*Toxicology*

Denial works six times faster than conventional varnish.
—*Hyperthick*

Locked room murder mysteries ask the question of how the victim was killed in a seemingly unbreached room locked from within. To whodunit addicts laying around in a clue-induced stupor, considerations of power in the universe at large are muted by attention to the absorbing details and parameters of the room, just as eighty years of a human life may pass without seeing its own context.
—*Heart of the Original*

"Know what I pray of a morning? That god should leave me alone if he can."
—*The Complete Accomplice*

I'm not trusting that pharmaceutical gumbo you've got for a brain.
—*Hyperthick*

What with the hazards of drugs, sex and spiritual quest, crime was one of the few activities a young man could undertake without fear of the consequences.
—*The Crime Studio*

In the pantheon of archetypes, only the trickster doesn't run on rails—it zigzags across others' stories, self-starting and unreactive. It was first delineated, in fact, to contain "everything else" which scholars and ancient storytellers couldn't manage to think up and symbolise in the other archetypes. Since these scribes were chronically unimaginative, the bulk of the universe's more interesting facts and possibilities ended up in the trickster.
—*Heart of the Original*

Heinlein was increasingly hobbled by a political conservatism for which he never sought treatment.
—*Hyperthick*

Truth isn't beguiled, people are. Truth remains whether anyone's gazing that way or not. It's the most patient thing in the world.
—*The Complete Accomplice*

A great deal of what passes for philosophy is the elaborately decked-out cry of someone falling over.
—*Johnny Viable*

Age is not care, starvation is not understatement, thoughts are not invocations.
—*The Complete Accomplice*

An elephant mended
is a tusker befriended;
an elephant dead
is as big as a shed.
—*Lint*

An eclipse clicked into place like an optician's test lens.
—*Novahead*

You may bump into the devil when tracing the circumference of a penny.
—*Hyperthick*

Society's harassments are not always deterred by death—some of those guillotined in the late nineteenth century found their heads being hectored by scientists eager to see if the victim's eyes would swivel at their tormentors. The eyes did respond, fixing the scientists with a stare of stony resolve as if at the last straw. Miscreants of disciplined character sought to bring enough air into the mouth before severance that when the detached head was raised triumphantly to the crowd it might utter a single word. A favourite was: "And?"
—*Heart of the Original*

At every action ask yourself, "Why feel ineffectual when my very frustration advances the world cause?"
—*Toxicology*

I'll fall in with any scheme that has me dressed as an otter, as you know.
—*Hyperthick*

The story depicts a collector of religious relics, much like Volospion himself. The old man in the story has several of Christ's anklebones, at least a dozen of his fingers, gallons of his blood, three of his skulls at various stages of development and so on. He determines to piece them together into a Tauksaw, a re-assembled body, the ultimate object of worship. In his cloistered chamber he thinks he hears the faintest "click" with each incorporation. Of course, at last the result is a monster. An

incoherent mass of fraud, fakery, lies, deception, self-deception and even honest delusion. It rears up, each patch carving one against another. The old man is horrified. "What are you?" he demands. "You have achieved what I never quite achieved in life," states the abomination. "I asked," the old man repeats, "what are you?" "I am what you have made me," says the freak. "What?" asks the old man. "A liar? A pointless mess? A justification for anything?" "Yes," says the figure. "A man."
—*Rebel at the End of Time*

He was distracted from his work on *Betty Carbon* one afternoon by the feeling of peculiar eternities—years in a minute he was staring at the blank page and when he finally turned to look at the room, an alien totem pole carved from angelskin coral and klieg marble had taken up residence. Around it hurtled feedback angels and battering photons, minds endless and dense irradiating the room. Cathedric creatures, entities in knots and tesseract nations defied the scale of the house with gem infinities.
—*Lint*

Revelations are rare. I've had a bare half dozen in the last ten years.
—*Johnny Viable*

Any act worth a damn cannot be ignored and when an effective person is ignored it's the result of a deliberate series of steps.
—*Slaughtermatic*

Disagreement, to a true believer, is easily tolerated. The boundaries of organised religion are military.
—*Heart of the Original*

An unstable warlock shouldn't be boring but you've done it.
—*Hyperthick*

Pick out summer from a picnic and you're left with idiots in a marsh.
—*The Inflatable Volunteer*

The "bungled reception of technology" which we allow to shape us—I take the Easter Island extinction as an example. All 887 moai statues looked inland, so that the Rapa Nui people had inadvertently created a surveillance society which drove them to a frenzy of judgement and annihilation.
—*Heart of the Original*

Do my arms deceive me?
—*Hyperthick*

Without connective tissue this universe would be the size of a pea, and good riddance.
—*Hyperthick*

Kennedy would flicker his eyelids rapidly when Hoover entered the room in order to give the little man's movements a visually "Chaplinesque" quality.
—*Lint*

Pretension—the pretence that your words or actions are of greater value or meaning than they actually are.
—*Toxicology*

Look at old Nobbo. His pants are made of pewter, his arms are stiff and he has surrendered control of his face to others—tee hee!
—*The Caterer*

They're pious out of weariness or mere lack of imagination.
—*Johnny Viable*

It was the fashion to punish crooks severely so as to encourage their assimilation back into the underworld—a process known as "recrimination."
—*The Crime Studio*

Reviews are read as if afraid of art that arrives unescorted.
—*Heart of the Original*

Cheap harm lasts just as long.
—*The Complete Accomplice*

"Trickles whisper in abattoir drains and all's well with the world."
—*The Inflatable Volunteer*

Murder with an oar, staple of the opportunist.
—*Hyperthick*

Describe social custom with care—you may give something away.
—*The Complete Accomplice*

When relaxing outside the "Goldilocks zone" of tolerated zaniness, your bespoke insecurities will make others' look all the more off-the-peg and cause an anxiety with no name.
—*Heart of the Original*

A one-track god is easily avoided.
—*Smithereens*

The secret splendor of purpose, a tattooed heart!
—*Hyperthick*

To smoke a cigar while being tortured is the ultimate gesture.
—*The Complete Accomplice*

They built churches but would later concede that god had eluded the cordon.
—*Hyperthick*

No end of friends but gets through the embalming fluid, know what I mean?
—*The Inflatable Volunteer*

The co-existence of lobsters and chefs suggests a dispiriting sort of order.
—*Hyperthick*

You make more difference to the world painting a wall than you do writing satire.
—*The Complete Accomplice*

"Crime is an evolving definition sir—and one must evolve with the times."
—*Atom*

The clerk tripped on the carpet, hit a window and went through, carrying with him a vase which had been on the sill. His skull broke like the vase and the vase broke like his skull, and both burst forth water mainly, and from the vase some flowers. If I could choose a death I'd make it something like that, except I'd add a good woman and some lard.
—*The Inflatable Volunteer*

He had an irregular object in the centre of his face. I could only explain it as some sort of nostril array.
—*Novahead*

My affinity with the rolling fragments of paradise puts me at a disadvantage socially. But this precision of mine, which is ruining my relationships, is the golden glory of my life.
—*Hyperthick*

It's said that upon discovery of the 8000 terracotta soldiers under China's Shaanxi province, one of the figures was doing something interesting. The accounts vary between mere squatting in a sarcastic way to extruding a foliate superstructure from its shoulders on which were inscribed the Zodiac of False Assumptions: that the space occupied by any human body is more interesting than that which is not, that all happiness is the same colour, that after getting worse things will get better, that the world will end when humanity does, that it's a long way to twist to see your own soul and so on. Ignored by the sentinels around it for two millennia, it's now valued above gold in the strange auburn market of antimundane contraband and is reputedly with a private collector in Novosibirsk.
—*Heart of the Original*

True but useless, like a foreign coin.
—*Hyperthick*

I began presenting myself as an honorable man. Unfortunately I chose to do the impersonation in one of the world's most treacherous shipping lanes.
—*Hyperthick*

"What do you get if you cross a barber with a camel?"
    "I don't know, what do you get if you cross a barber with a camel?"
    "An abomination."
—*The Complete Accomplice*

I witnessed a whale weeping tears the size of lightbulbs.
—*Hyperthick*

"I am authorised to do ample justice to every villain but myself."
—*Rebel at the End of Time*

Some think I'm a bad guy, but is anyone defined without cost?
—*Hyperthick*

"All I have learned are the divers arts of the cornered man: snarling, begging, screaming, sobbing, whispering, fainting, feinting, painting, panting, ranting and, of course, sitting down."
    "It sounds like being cornered is an education in itself."
    "And cheap. Remember that."
—*Fain the Sorcerer*

He fell into his seat with a gasp and sat resembling almost exactly the portrait behind him, in which he looked like a lump of scorched dough.
—*The Complete Accomplice*

The edge of my opinion slots exactly into the edge of yours. Don't you wanna see the whole jigsaw?
—*Hyperthick*

I was careless enough to be born in England. I'm not about to compound the error by dying here.
—*Shamanspace*

Dumb people cast an honest shadow.
—*The Complete Accomplice*

Confessed to a priest who remained doggedly celestial despite all I was telling him. The entire affair was a waste of time.
—*Toxicology*

"Why have a king anyway?"
    "Well if you must have evil you want it localized and eating lark."
—*Hyperthick*

"You a man or a mouse?"
    "I appear to be allowed the understanding of the latter."
—*Bigot Hall*

Anarchism's sense of responsibility scares you doesn't it? Those who do what they're told had better look to their souls.
—*Hyperthick*

An interrogation is not just a form of emotional feasting; it's really a form of divination. Its arcane conditions are supposed to conjure information that none of those taking part actually know.
—*Novahead*

Lint's disappointment at the wasted possibilities exemplified in the resolutely mediocre, and his suspicion of the motives of fear and evasion behind that resoluteness make for strong and heady works.
—*And Your Point Is?*

An assumption about the universe is that everything is included, but its tendency to divide and particularise suggests it is seeking novelty.
—*Heart of the Original*

"Anything my legs can pass, I'll ignore."
—*Toxicology*

Any description of a great truth will reduce it, like describing a ship by its anchor. But even at a hint we're sent storming to our polarities with hands over our ears. Stubbornness is not wise—it has no other qualities than itself. Stubbornness is not wisdom or courage.
—*Lint*

If we accept that reptiles have a way of knowing their own smooth charm, should we trouble ourselves with any other question?
—*The Inflatable Volunteer*

"I'm increasingly convinced that this space-time axis is entirely ornamental."
—*Novahead*

Style reinforces anger in Lint's stories and what may appear as serious defects in style from one critical vantage become logical moves from another, depending on the reader's knowledge of history and power dynamics. Lint is unashamedly aware of these matters and his style is inextricably tied to his world-view, his conception of a mess of a planet lashed around with man-made chains. Indeed, Lint's works have been characterized by Lewis Tambs as "Bitter Baroque."
—*And Your Point Is?*

Lazy obedience is a unit of entropy. Entropy is high because there are countless dismal acquiescences to fall into and only one or two very focussed and specific manoeuvres by which to maintain yourself.
—*Heart of the Original*

Without us, gardens won't stop.
—*Johnny Viable*

"I just saw a snail. Checkmate I think you'll find."
—*Hyperthick*

I found myself hungering for the wooden stone at the heart of the peach, a truth which didn't change from one moment to the next.
—*Toxicology*

I think I am correct in saying that a meal of this standard is a criminal offence. Saying thank you for it is like ceremonially forgiving the headsman before his work.
—*The Complete Accomplice*

Disorder's an offence with no mappable contours and the ideal fog for all occasions.
—*Toxicology*

I've learnt that a man must go where he's welcome if he wishes for conviviality, and where he's unwelcome if he wishes for mayhem and adventure.
—*The Inflatable Volunteer*

The oldest lies get the highest polish.
—*Hyperthick*

When I was a kid the devout sang a chorus of subordination and villains wore masks to keep off the glare of our envy.
—*The Inflatable Volunteer*

From space this Earth is incandescent with abominations—the gods write their signature in our entrails.
—*The Inflatable Volunteer*

Of course the government want us to kick heroin. And they're not asking us to do anything they haven't done themselves.
—*Lint*

A yellow dragon. I was yomped into its huge mouth in four swallows, head last. And still wasn't "in the moment."
—*Hyperthick*

In the middle of the twentieth century, palaeontologists found a small dinosaur fossil *Coelophysis* inside a larger fossil *Coelophysis*, and wondered whether it was a case of gestation or cannibalism. The same question will occur to those who find human fossils in the ruins of our cities.
—*Heart of the Original*

The area was famous for the cops' planting of drugs and users had begun flocking there in the hope of being able to keep some in exchange for violence.
—*Toxicology*

Wooden skulls don't work for long.
—*The Inflatable Volunteer*

Doors were invented to let people in and out, and as long as doors were included in the design of safes, vaults and houses, they would continue to serve this purpose.
—*The Crime Studio*

Solutions vanish every second of every day and we will never know the geniuses lost to the cubicle or to cops in a burst of taser confetti.
—*Heart of the Original*

I read the book that night at my leisure. It would have blown the eyebrows off a portrait of Jesus.
—*Hyperthick*

I called my dog "Machine Gun Charlie" and believed in something called a "Wishing Shark." I had no idea I was based on a real person. Wild times.
—*Johnny Viable*

Reparation? Authority after the fact is no authority at all.
—*Lint*

You cannot ice-skate and be bewildered at the same time.
—*The Inflatable Volunteer*

Driven by fraudulent intensities installed at no great cost, you'll run into the fire of your own free will.
—*Hyperthick*

If you don't have a fridge, store your food in the mirror. Granted it'll invert and stink of mirror, but those times when everyone is wrong are powerful times.
—*Hyperthick*

Gamete set up a news service in which all the facts were guaranteed true. Subscribers had to pay through the nose but the other networks damned it nevertheless as unfair competition—cost wasn't the issue.
—*Slaughtermatic*

Do a thing carefully and nobody cares. But make a big noise?
—*Hyperthick*

Demons. They can appear as fast cracks driving through walls, plans and mourners. They'll have your shoulders cramped with meetings, reduce your thinking to the market.
—*The Complete Accomplice*

The thingness of a gun, its weight, the disastrous potential in the stillness of its moving parts. Pound for pound it was tragic as charred pollen.
—*Novahead*

Consensus is reality with the crusts cut off.
—*The Complete Accomplice*

Death came so close I saw the inside of its jacket and I became straightforward practically overnight.
—*Hyperthick*

"Two positives can't make a negative."
   "Yeah, right."
—*The Complete Accomplice*

Only the most contorted artifice could manifest this unimaginable combination of sterility and necrotic corruption. It told of existence as a hammer, repeated doses of the same day, replacing hours with the same hours, a desolation of such repetitive detail that I was almost mad with its ceaselessness.
—*Smithereens*

"The moss'll be growing in my name before I'm appreciated."
—*The Complete Accomplice*

Thought truth was the stone in the snowball. Truth was really the whole shebang.
—*Shamanspace*

When man cannot effect cannibalism, can only be judged by evils, as distant cities go quiet in collapse and trouble, I will make toast by the river, and remember the warning I gave you this day.
—*The Inflatable Volunteer*

Wounds close without fanfare.
—*The Complete Accomplice*

Gaps grow together and we've got a meaning—call that culture?
—*The Complete Accomplice*

The almost-forgotten cramp of youth is a combination of sourness and postponement.
—*Rebel at the End of Time*

To live past hope, like walking into thin air ...
—*Smithereens*

"She had one of those smiles that went upside-down, using all the muscles," said Lint. "It worked her whole face. She wasn't afraid to crack her mask."
—*Lint*

The parable of the great banquet, in which the diners' arms are splinted and fitted with forks four feet long so that they cannot reach the food up to their mouths, leads to the obvious solution of the diners feeding each other and then hunting down and punishing whoever set up this diabolical torture so that it cannot happen to others. After all, they're armed. But though we all think it, I have never seen the "punishment" phase of the operation suggested in print. Our manners make for tragedy.
—*Heart of the Original*

Be careful which public enemy you invent; it may begin to exist.
—*The Complete Accomplice*

Wow, speculation doesn't disappoint.
—*Hyperthick*

My rule for life is to be desperate *one day at a time*.
—*The Inflatable Volunteer*

"Our despair's so comprehensive round here it'll take more than your miracles to shift it Padre."
—*The Inflatable Volunteer*

I owed no morality to those who would extort it by force.
—*Slaughtermatic*

Live long enough and we travel over a million brinks, becoming numb to fear or safety.
—*Hyperthick*

You'll be outdistanced by the universe always.
—*Hyperthick*

The pause allowed me to circumnavigate her arguments and look back at my own—the entire vista left a lot to be desired. I was some sort of clog-wearing hen.
—*Novahead*

Certain minutes are like a doughnut, the very thing. Sitting on a bare plinth, Chloe gazed at toppled pillars, drifting air silk and world light. A tree whisked around, Barny's dog Help capered near a basilisk platform, earth rust was baked by the sun. Here was a bush before the wind, the drained blue table under the wall, the bottomless sky, and amazing silence. And Barny was gazing bovine at Chloe, her smile longer by inches, watching the girl shift buttocks and squint at the sky. In this strange corpse orchard, a vast plain of pillared people, his heart ripened and peached.

—*The Complete Accomplice*

Only a puzzle with defined edges can be solved.

—*The Complete Accomplice*

German jokes don't have much of a whipcrack because their syntax puts the punchline in the middle.

—*Hyperthick*

The competing polarities were malice and accident. The former credo stated that we live in a sudden universe of bleak power and malevolence, a trick so big and simple it surrounds us up to and including the cells of our bodies; subordination on the grandest scale we know. The latter posited that god created the universe in a blaze of negligence. The error theory had a subsect theorizing that god had a nonbiological gameplan which was derailed by organic life. Though most people believed there was not enough irony stored in the rest-mass of the universe to account for a god of any kind, I confess I had recently been giving a superficial nod to errorverse ritual. Everything I observed confirmed that we were living in the endless aftermath of a mistake.

—*Novahead*

For some, belief is lodged too close to the heart to be removed safely.

—*Heart of the Original*

The trouble with the law is that it's yet to fall into the right hands.

—*Slaughtermatic*

Look simultaneously at the horizon and the detail in coins. There's a test of perspective.
—*The Complete Accomplice*

England's a shower curtain for the modest butcher.
—*The Inflatable Volunteer*

America, an empire with its heart in its jaws.
—*Heart of the Original*

Standing amid a society that mimics personal power and "choice" above all, he can barely draw breath for laughing—while the constant allowances he must make while moving through this vacuum of dishonesty has forced the bones of his head to bulge out sideways like a faulty vase. In a way, he is using his own skull as a sort of space helmet.
—*And Your Point Is?*

He began quick-drawing the peace sign like a six-shooter, an act so startling that people would flinch and forget what they were saying.
—*Lint*

And if, years after my body's entrusted to the drenched earth, my lower jaw falls with a dull click, quick bugs will enjoy it like an obstacle course.
—*Hyperthick*

The roof exists only to conceal what the world is about to heap upon me.
—*The Inflatable Volunteer*

I'll eat anything if it's baked to perfection!
—*Hyperthick*

Catholicism, the etiquette from outer space.
—*Hyperthick*

Injustice rings down through history to a deserted callbox.
—*Toxicology*

Clauses dissolve in any soil, given time, and every pictogram uncoils to a straight line.
—*Hyperthick*

I'm serenaded by bullshit.
—*The Inflatable Volunteer*

Pythagoras believed in reincarnation and stopped someone beating a dog because he recognised in its barking the cries of a friend. A better man would have stopped it upon recognising in its barking the cries of a dog.
—*Heart of the Original*

He was the type who would act all high and mighty and then eat something too hot and end up drinking out of a vase.
—*The Crime Studio*

Time is central to life. Anything which is a process, requires the dimension of time. Flowers require it, for instance. Only something which is fixed and finished does not. Is it coincidental that when a thing is complete and fixed, as in a museum, all life goes out of it?
—*Fain the Sorcerer*

As a precaution I shout "Beware!" when I enter a new location. That's a real hammerblow for anyone having a nice time.
—*Hyperthick*

You're chortling, you think you know a secret. Then you forget the secret, you forget you ever chortled, you make a sandwich. You get older and mirrors choke your smile.
—*The Complete Accomplice*

"The truth at low tide, complications revealed."
—*Hyperthick*

"What do our standards mean? A wolf thinks it's clean."
—*Hyperthick*

"What's that hidden in his euphoria?"

"It looks exactly like a religious charlatan's earnest tension!"

—*Lint*

I was incredibly horny when I was a young 'un—smoke the colour of biscuit came out of my nose when I saw the curvature on a woman. I was calm only when knocked oblivious by a restaurant swingdoor and how often does that really happen?

—*The Inflatable Volunteer*

Vampires consider us a beverage.

—*Hyperthick*

"If absolutely everyone saw things differently, the world would become total variegation without duplication—chaos."

"Interesting," Leo mulled, "in other words."

—*Rebel at the End of Time*

I haven't forgotten for a single moment that I'm a puppet. How could I, with all that outside influence?

—*Hyperthick*

Don't think of it as a problem, but as a challenge which has defeated you.

—*Lint*

A fascist nation is one which has forced itself to a conclusion.

—*Heart of the Original*

Just as K.'s shame at being subject to the state's edicts cripple him to the point of accepting them in Kafka's *The Trial*, to admit the truth would require action or shame.

—*Heart of the Original*

It's a myth that revolution isn't fun—there are forged papers, rain, and monologues in the interval.

—*The Complete Accomplice*

As speechgiver, raconteur and sudden bellower from windows the Mayor's oeuvre contained a good many classics including "I Serve You Though You Sicken Me," "Look at the State of You," "This Sea of Gawking Faces" and the more mature, resigned tone of "I Realise I'm Stranded Here." Among policy speeches were "I Will Destroy All Other Candidates," "Burn, You Mother" and the hardline "I Will Make It More Expensive," as well as the sympathy bid "I Kick Snails Away But They Keep on Coming" during which Rudloe collapsed into quiet tears. "Hello, Mate" and "You Will Become Dust" played well both in their separate forms and as the combination barnstormer "Hello, Mate—You Will Become Dust." Other philosophical and contemplative monologues were "Bang—Sorrow!," "Am I Really So Chubby?" and "My Thirteen Thousand Misgivings," an epic diatribe about everyone he remembered seeing or meeting. His personal favourites were the boastful "Trousers Won't Contain It," the pugnacious "Yes, This Is My Eleventh Corned Beef Sandwich," the truculent "Lurk Here, Lurk There, You Champion Bastards" and the knockabout nonsense of "Arly-Barley Fell Me Where I Stand." He even displayed some humour in the safety talks "Head—Don't Travel Without One!" and "Thank God For Chainmail," and the left cheek of his arse in "Get a Load of This."
—*The Complete Accomplice*

Long ago, atoms like hints assembling—ten headstrong atoms is a good enough start for life.
—*Hyperthick*

the nightmare's likely to renew until the day humanity rests finally in lavender and ruins, becoming one big last outbreath. Patience.
—*Smithereens*

It's a golden age for border guards.
—*Hyperthick*

Critics abhorred Algren's pointing out flaws and proposing no solutions, on the odd grounds that a man unable to stop a fire himself should not presume to alert anyone else.
—*Heart of the Original*

Lint continued to experiment. Inspired by Gex's poem about events in Chile in 1974, *Santiago*, in which a first-hand description of the US-backed massacre of 9/11 was simply divided up into lines, Lint did a similar thing with Kissinger's green light to Suharto's genocide in East Timor:

The use of US-made arms
could create problems
our risks of being found out
our efficiency is cut
our main concern is that whatever you do
does not create a climate
that discourages investment
we will do our best to keep everyone quiet
until the president returns home.
—*Lint*

"Is this what passes for murder round here?"
—*Toxicology*

Not all colors are in the dictionary.
—*Lint*

"You'll have no physical pain Eddie, not at first. Life measured in tides of snot, whispered like memorial curses. Movement by the tiny privilege stepladder. Dark afflicted years of assignment to the business corridor, then the last."
—*The Inflatable Volunteer*

He'll do till a dog comes along.
—*Hyperthick*

The self-divided universe, separated to observe itself. In its jaws happiness and torment are known side by side like the seconds in a minute.
—*Rebel at the End of Time*

Born on Pancake Day and downhill from there!
—*Hyperthick*

In Plato's allegory of the cave, the realm of waiters exists outside, but it is only their shadows, cast by an unseen source of light onto the cave wall, that erstwhile diners inside can see.
—*And Your Point Is?*

Of all life's instants, being ejected from a job interview one backward step at a time, each step provoked by a punch upside the face from the interviewer, is one tailor made for grim reflection.
—*The Complete Accomplice*

I've seen more volition in the eyes of a potato.
—*Hyperthick*

Lint's relationship with Dewhurst finally reached an end with Lint's 1960 story "Feelgood," in which the hero awakes *Day of the Triffids*-style to find the world empty of people and wanders blissfully free of harassment for the rest of his life. The character's transition from cautious optimism to boundless joy is superbly handled, though Dewhurst removed several scenes where the protagonist spontaneously climaxes while walking down the deserted streets.
—*Lint*

Real friends don't shake hands.
—*The Complete Accomplice*

As with most public figures she has a morality like a fake eye on the wing of a moth.
—*Hyperthick*

"Die, Atom!" he yelled, a stricture I found impossible to take seriously. Afterwards, ofcourse, I saw that his plan to shoot me was a good one.
—*Novahead*

By way of apology I did a tropical dance with fruit on my head. And just in my underpants. Boy it did not go well.
—*Hyperthick*

She wore her veins in a ponytail.
—*The Complete Accomplice*

When the mind has to jump a gap, the spark it fires can tickle the brain's surface or ignite unused pathways, depending on the guidelines placed on either side. Poets use the same dodge by staking images on either side of a feeling they cannot point to or describe directly.
—*Heart of the Original*

One morning Elsa snapped at him "You're selfish" and Lint, thinking she'd said "Your shellfish," sat waiting for her to present him with some sort of seafood platter. After ten silent, staring minutes he demanded "Well? Where are the clams?" and Elsa went into the bedroom to pack her stuff.
—*Lint*

"We are claiming this festivity is more precious than it is—which lights up our eyes with love. When all the while it's as good as stealing from you. Light up with simplicity, all! Inhale from flasks! Move many limbs at once! Madness onrushing! We celebrate!"
—*The Complete Accomplice*

A school is a scruffy laying-hutch for evil.
—*Hyperthick*

When all history's lessons have been given, it begins to cycle.
—*The Complete Accomplice*

Many sages advise against a surprise ending but fail to say where the surprise should be. Do they mean a story should include nothing we don't already know, or that the whole thing should be a surprise?
—*Heart of the Original*

Human beings are so short-lived they die before they've come to their senses, and I've come to think it's the same for the species as a whole.
—*Novahead*

Whittemore, the hero of Lint's consciously Asimov-styled short "The Robot Who Couldn't Be Bothered," appears indistinguishable from other robots (and humans) until given an order—at this point it is discovered that his inactivity is the result of "eleven million nodes of personal consideration." Lint, too, appeared inconspicuous until ordered to do something—at which point, groin beware.
—*And Your Point Is?*

Notice the ears on either side of that apple? *Now* tell me the world's not collapsing.
—*The Inflatable Volunteer*

"Life's a term of outlandish grief, bookended by white darkness, nothing more."
—*Hyperthick*

With our future ahead of us and our past behind, a manoeuvre to the sides, above or below might expose epic sweeps of terrain to explore, each sideline having different properties and climates.
—*Heart of the Original*

I don't like churches. Cutlery chain on the truth, or they'd like you to think so.
—*The Complete Accomplice*

I sold a spicy doughball in the street for eighty quid because the fool thought I was someone else. There was my first lesson in how to progress in this world.
—*The Inflatable Volunteer*

That night I looked out at the courtyard to see a pair of albino gill-men doing a sort of silent fandango.
—*Hyperthick*

Time is longer than hope.
—*Atom*

"Come nearer where I can ignore you."
—*The Complete Accomplice*

"We've all heard talk about 'interesting times.' Why aren't there ever times that are interesting in a nice way? Why isn't that a thing?"
    "What you're describing is mercy, and no, it's not a thing."
—*Hyperthick*

If you take a catfish by the whiskers and pull outwards, it inflates into a life-raft.
—*The Caterer*

Individual versus society, or versus god. Either way it's the resistance to absorption.
—*Shamanspace*

Remember our company motto: "A happy surface flattens living flowers."
—*Hyperthick*

"I'm not sure I follow the gallopede of shite you call an argument."
—*The Inflatable Volunteer*

He side-stepped the issue so fast he generated a small sonic boom.
—*Hyperthick*

Human beings find themselves part of an exploitative machine which adds insult to injury by being boring. For an illusion of a free world to convince for any length of time, the system projected should at least function theoretically, and this is where the current illusion fails.
—*And Your Point Is?*

The Hydra's most boring head yet.
—*Hyperthick*

My disappointment suffuses you I hope. Otherwise it's a waste.
—*Hyperthick*

Meanwhile, others dine on hailstones and sleep wretched behind a bone doorbell.
—*Hyperthick*

I'll die, and nature will probably be unsatisfied with rotting me once.
—*Novahead*

Some things you don't believe till you see them in the mirror.
—*Toxicology*

The truth drinks last, when everyone's gone home.
—*The Complete Accomplice*

"Hey Carl, you got the scoop on a tailspin saint who won a double to-morrow and sleeps without mercy?"
—*Hyperthick*

Stab me if you can enjoy it—but not if it feels like a duty. Stab me verti-cally if I'm lying down and horizontally if I'm running.
—*The Inflatable Volunteer*

My lawyer reeled into the room facing back toward the previous en-counter.
—*Hyperthick*

"Does he understand the moral component of the exercise?"
    "Is there one?"
    "The hole where it should be is the right shape. It'll do."
—*Novahead*

The authorities portrayed shock and outrage but never described what it was they had been expecting.
—*Slaughtermatic*

A mind too clogged to rattle or discern.
—*Hyperthick*

The Bible's all small print.
—*Toxicology*

Lint rushed around to the studio to strangle the reserved Englishman. "He didn't seem to know how to do it," Turnour said years later. "Instead of strangling my neck, he sort of grabbed me around the middle of my head, squeezing that. It surprised me, but it was hardly dangerous."
—*Lint*

"You did a horribly precise dance called the Stipulator, dainty as a prince on porcelain hooves. And after two hours scrutinizing a wall of only small interest to the sober man, you used a box jellyfish as a catapult."
—*Hyperthick*

"It seems that if anything stays still long enough, he'll befriend it. The man's drunk on his own power."
—*The Complete Accomplice*

Optimists viewed the law as no more than a desperate measure of continuity, until it began changing every week. Most then assumed the law was capricious because it varied with time, geography, funds, influence, interpretation and so on from one day to the next. But the motives for law are common and unchanging—that's the continuity.
—*Novahead*

I could not avoid noticing that popular patterns of salvation played to the expediencies of infrastructure ... And the dog has given its strongest indication yet that he hates me.
—*Hyperthick*

Each privation endured at least a thousand years; the progress of society was the forging of replacement shackles.
—*Rebel at the End of Time*

Tired of your abilities? Join the army.
—*The Complete Accomplice*

That skeleton on the parallel bars has practised hard—years to produce something which is, at best, expected.
—*Hyperthick*

"How much active ingredient?"
    "What I term a 'recognition of the problem.'"
    "Which is?"
    "A thousandth-of-a-percent of the solution."
—*Toxicology*

Dietrich was beginning to see how the new hell operated. This place worked like a jigsaw. Nothing would be a whole pain again.
—*The Complete Accomplice*

Templates can't stand a masterpiece.
—*The Complete Accomplice*

Free of fashion or lobbying, the authentic from-the-ground-up thought of the individual births the original.
—*Heart of the Original*

The reducing of people to something less than human allows evil full articulation of movement.
—*Hyperthick*

To the short of memory everything is unprecedented, and the rest are pressured to pretend.
—*Heart of the Original*

And I thought—parts become outdated, it's a hood with smile, it's sleeves on cars, it's the norm, who can keep up?
—*The Inflatable Volunteer*

He threw a punch that completely missed its target—an act known as an "airstrike."
—*Hyperthick*

Even a rose shoulders space for itself.
—*And Your Point Is?*

"When you're in a position where you must make unpopular, indeed disastrous, decisions every day, before you know it you've got chops like these." He pulled his cheeks out like empty pockets, then released them, giving up.
—*The Complete Accomplice*

Any good insolence accommodates whole universes.
—*The Complete Accomplice*

That head of yours can hardly be put to any sensible use.
—*Hyperthick*

Crossing lanes was an ambulance painted in black primer, driven by what appeared to be a tormented clown. *But is there any other kind,* I wondered.
—*Novahead*

Terror and dread, the claws of the soul—hang on for dear life.
—*Bigot Hall*

Flop out your wallets and pretend you've a choice.
—*The Complete Accomplice*

To exist as a peg between others' positions? Oh limpet! Oh urchin!
—*Hyperthick*

I seem to be embedded in the slave graduation carnival we call society. Last time I tried getting out I broke my arm and collarbone.
—*Johnny Viable*

Collaborate honestly at least. Acknowledge what you are giving and receiving.
—*Hyperthick*

Opposites attract, resulting in a narrowing of possibilities.
—*Slaughtermatic*

Such people are too calm to be taken seriously.
—*Heart of the Original*

Toto struck what he probably thought was a chastened pose but succeeded only in looking like an ape.
—*Novahead*

"Bring me your huddled masses and I'll adopt a look of fierce consideration."
—*The Complete Accomplice*

You don't often see frogs holding hands, but when you do, by god it's a day to remember.
—*Hyperthick*

When my parents taught me about the birds and the bees they simply stated that most of them were dead.
—*Hyperthick*

The English, a people with many bosses to feed and placate.
—*Heart of the Original*

Approval keeps the spine straight and the chin up, in a slave.
—*Novahead*

The Soviet principle of employment-as-identity now being applied in the West is the logical conclusion of economics theology grafted over the very short political spectrum beloved of most human beings.
—*Heart of the Original*

Capitalism is not a symmetrical affliction. Too often it depends on coincidence and a justice we know of only by report.
—*Heart of the Original*

The state stripped of crimes—not even a skeleton is left.
—*Smithereens*

Fascism is born of the notion that progress can reach a conclusion.
—*The Complete Accomplice*

It's a fragile conquest that bad manners can undo.
—*Shamanspace*

"I'll say to them, 'The fault lies not in your stars but yourselves.' The phrase'll put some mysterious starry influence in the place of us, as the manipulating force. It's a classic two-choice limitation statement, neither option being the accurate one. Pure distraction, beautiful."
—*The Complete Accomplice*

There are moments when even a honeybee doesn't see the point.
—*Hyperthick*

Couldn't believe what I was expected to do. Breathe constantly. Talk to those who addressed me, merely because they addressed me. This was life? What could I do with these legs and this face except kick and curse those I encountered?
—*The Inflatable Volunteer*

In the universal war the sides are countless, variations infinite, and the only evil is to conceal this. A true sense of humour has the ability to dance with adversity.
—*The Nerve*

We bring death and those who claim to be our rivals bring death also. It's investing everywhere.
—*Toxicology*

The architecture of circumstance rarely fits a soul's journey, it's all jabs and discomfort like a creature in the wrong shell.
—*Hyperthick*

Kindness is the sun that was left out of our sky.
—*Hyperthick*

The landfill of masks will never happen.
—*Toxicology*

Tom Hull relates a conversation he had with Lint in Santa Fe in 1987, at the end of which "His features shot into squares, receding at speed. Funny way to leave it."
—*Lint*

Don't unravel them—your ears are meant to be that way.
—*The Complete Accomplice*

"What happened to faith in a higher authority?"
  "Burned in a wicker man?"
—*Toxicology*

Startling the moment a good luck atom falls thru you.
—*Hyperthick*

Extra! Extra! Big fella harbors no illusions! Attaches concrete ears to White House!
—*Johnny Viable*

Meanwhile someone stepped into a cage with a lion. For me a lion is like any other situation—if you're going to whip it and push it away with a chair, why get involved in the first place?
—*Bigot Hall*

"You can interpret people through intolerance and get whatever you want at the other end. Now that's a bargain!"
—*Hyperthick*

Even his brain's got a tan.
—*The Crime Studio*

A dictator's justifications have so little objective reality they have practically no natural enemies.
—*Heart of the Original*

Unachieved, my destiny drums its bony fingers as I snore.
—*The Inflatable Volunteer*

Old people aren't automatically wise, though all are adept at a judgemental stare as if apprised of souls.
—*Heart of the Original*

His philosophy was the most complete fossil of its kind ever found.
—*Novahead*

"Killjar brothers date their dreams, the horizon wounds like a knife, pebbles surge in roil-whispers—and other calculated marvels. Don't try bullshitting me, brother."
—*The Inflatable Volunteer*

The public image of The Author—ramrod straight, unsurprised and studded with snails that make a popping sound when removed—has given way to the general impression of a force intent on using as many words as possible to say nothing we don't already know.
—*Smithereens*

The multiverse model has universes budding off fractally, encapsulated like the linked floatation bladders of seaweed. Some Pacific cultures eat bladderwrack with a butter sauce to indicate their position on the matter.
—*Heart of the Original*

"You disgust me."
    "And I will tomorrow."
—*Hyperthick*

The future will arrive when everyone has forgotten about it.
—*The Complete Accomplice*

"Have you heard of the Turing test, Mr Atom—to determine if someone is a real human being? If they try and convict you for no crime, chemically castrate you and drive you to suicide despite your being instrumental in winning their war, they're human."
—*Novahead*

There's no "I" in team. Nor in death, trouble or bouncy.
—*Hyperthick*

That all of us are the subconscious thought impulses of a shabby god. That many of us want to die. These were the truth-halves of one picture.
—*Shamanspace*

"Accusations eh? Simply change his statement to something untrue and refute that."

"Announce the decision as if making it required courage. Show them a struggle."

"When things are fine, instil dread. When there's a real threat, urge calm. It's all control."

"To convince them of A, tell them they believe A. Then try to convert them to B and give up, beaten."

"Say that Americans don't understand. Yes, innocent simplicity, people will love that pretence in you and in themselves."
—*The Nerve*

Humanity was a species tested so long it should have fallen into baffled despair rather than its present million contradictory positions of utter certainty.
—*Novahead*

The risk of characterising your god as an insecure ruler is that you'll mistake an insecure ruler for your god.
—*Hyperthick*

Duplicated into the mind, a fact becomes a plaything.
—*Hyperthick*

"What'll you do about the economic crisis?"

"I'll internalise it, then I can move all the pieces around in me as if it was real. What happens outside, in reality, is your problem."
—*Johnny Viable*

A thing is deemed sacred when there's reason to keep us from dusting for fingerprints.
—*The Complete Accomplice*

He imagined his debut underground: "My first day in the reverse-nursery of the grave!"
—*Lint*

Dunk the year in dove paint, does that mean peace?
—*The Complete Accomplice*

"Why defend the self-evident?"

"Because it has enemies."
—*Hyperthick*

Through our answers runs the pest of truth.
—*The Complete Accomplice*

Angel refineries stood like gravestones and rotten hearts were piled in the sabotage yard.
—*The Complete Accomplice*

Running berserk leaves me in great shape and feeling special!
—*Hyperthick*

When Mardo was buried his coffin was filled with moths because some people thought he liked them and others thought he hated them.
—*Johnny Viable*

I saw a ghost once, a haughty smudge that made it hard to see the telly.
—*Hyperthick*

There prevails an unbroken harmony among those who enjoy strangling clowns.
—*The Complete Accomplice*

I consulted a law book, the contents of which I found to resemble the ravings of a lone crackpot.
—*Novahead*

"A cosmos of restrictions implies clarity of purpose, Terry. You're an optimist."
—*Hyperthick*

Male cops were taught it was okay to shoot a woman in the back but most still considered this too much of a commitment.
—*Slaughtermatic*

Invoking a remnant in place of rumination? How does your self-respect re-enter? I don't get it.
—*Johnny Viable*

That's the white game, stretching tradition over its skull like a stocking.
—*Hyperthick*

They saw discovered knowledge ignored for millennia until fashion's schedule decreed it could be acknowledged. They glimpsed erstwhile guardians who slumbered through slavery, legislators coining liberties with the implied right to withhold them, and always a majority willing to submit.
—*Rebel at the End of Time*

Admiration's a hindrance, luckily the dames hate me.
—*Hyperthick*

There was a time when the activity of swapping one addiction for another was the only example of fair barter remaining in the western world.
—*Slaughtermatic*

"Oh you know, the sea bubbling a tumble of skulls, forgotten clots of history resurfacing to our shame, a million years emerging, mastheads breaking the surface of the water, running the blades against a twilight sky, thoughts spilling into the sea foam and streaming from flapwind sails, that sort of thing. Eyes slamming open in the bellowing hull."
—*The Inflatable Volunteer*

A man whose lungs burst at the first sign of trouble.
—*Hyperthick*

Revolutionaries feel a need to explain their acts—dictators do not. You can even track the transition from one to the other in this need to be understood.
—*Rebel at the End of Time*

The irony in making allowances for police stupidity because they have a difficult job to do ...
—*Hyperthick*

It's degrading to endure the repeated expansions and restrictions of culture, like moving thru the chambers of a bowel. The assumption seems to be that I can't move along on my own.
—*Hyperthick*

The downside was at regular intervals he'd be hauled out of bed and propelled through a hull door with only a parachute between him and the slamming palm of god.
—*The Inflatable Volunteer*

The brain nature provided him remains unclaimed in his skull.
—*The Complete Accomplice*

Helterpolitik—the system of politics in Accomplice and the real world, composed of nanosecond memory, hypocrisy too extreme to process and pretended surprise at the consequences.
—*Accomplice A-Z*

People even take sides in an all-round failure.
—*Hyperthick*

Nature hates a vacuum and tends to fill it with the standing idle.
—*The Crime Studio*

The bee-like clumsiness of honesty is rarely appreciated.
—*Hyperthick*

Here were incoherent clashes in roads and fields, massacres without drama or remembrance.
—*Rebel at the End of Time*

A glass smashes and the world goes on.
—*Hyperthick*

The apparent lack of receptor points for the original to plug into is only in people's minds. In the absence of fear, the mind has as many orifices as it wants.
—*Heart of the Original*

Everything comes with a reason not to do it.
—*The Complete Accomplice*

Ideas are self-replenishing, like snot.
—*The Crime Studio*

When excluded from human society, don't stop to get it in writing. You are free.
—*Heart of the Original*

Cornered by clowns, I understood at last.
—*Hyperthick*

"When danger rears its bright face, the wise will run, the mad embrace."
—*Toxicology*

Life's a carousel with skeleton horses. —*Bigot Hall*

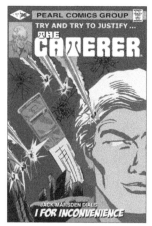

Paradox results from artificial boundaries. —*Lint*

I'm the skeleton you strain to conceal in your own body.
—*Slaughtermatic*

Television is light filled with someone else's anxiety.
—*Lint*

By the time I arrived in this world a thousand generations had already licked the jam out of the donut.
—*Hyperthick*

Humanity's choices were so scrupulously bad at every stage that it seemed these could not have been selected by chance or accident; their sabotages so intricate, they could not have been performed absent-mindedly.
—*Rebel at the End of Time*

There's an old Persian saying, "A flea won't be chained to an oar." Don't make yourself conspicuous.
—*Lint* (not an old Persian saying)

To spit out the pips of this world and move on ...
—*Hyperthick*

The comparison of monsters with one-another does not decrease their population. Evil clarified remains evil, and those who delineate it get their hands dirty.
—*Heart of the Original*

You can't discuss *helterpolitik* without sinking up to your face in it.
—*Novahead*

The heart of political power, chambered and smelly.
—*Hyperthick*

Vicars are able to re-grow their ears, did you know that?
—*Hyperthick*

Chum, I'm stood here the risen Christ. A cigarette in each nostril, I save time for myself and others. Clams yawn like a garbage truck as I approach with an opener. The embassy summon me and call me *bastardo*, slapping my face with my own passport.
—*The Inflatable Volunteer*

Swing a shrunken head by the hair and pitch it over a wall into someone's garden. The reward thenceforth, and for the rest of your life, is in your secret imagining.
—*Hyperthick*

Holding chemically opposite resentments with complementary domains, the individual and the law went forward together. When the individual died, what happened?
—*Novahead*

The system's defenders assert that it works on an assumption of benevolence. Such benevolence finds no support in observed phenomena.
—*Heart of the Original*

American friendly fire is rightly feared throughout the world.
—*Heart of the Original*

When I came to the critical point in my pitch their expression would alter completely. Nameless men would put me on to the street and continue to hold me down as if they feared I would otherwise float away. And afterward, looking up, I would see the executive staring down at me from the twentieth floor, his expression a concentrated dot of incredulity.
—*The Inflatable Volunteer*

Excessive confrontation is a kind of evasion.
—*Lint*

It's an odd match, sky and legislation. I suspect at least one of them is not aware of the other.
—*Hyperthick*

Among the honest, a whisper is the same as a declaration.
—*The Complete Accomplice*

Genius is like a pause—transplant it and it loses meaning.
—*The Complete Accomplice*

The ideal is to take the hypocrisy far enough beyond measure that people are left behind, measuring it with their standard ruler while the hyper-hypocrisy is free to play way out on the bell curve. Unalloyed capitalism: an idea that is correct in the minds of its victims.
—*Rebel at the End of Time*

Violation at varied angles is not creativity.
—*Hyperthick*

"Small head, soon led?" It's a cliché I know, but easy to remember.
—*Johnny Viable*

The supposed weird fringes are the only place honesty can find asylum. Real shock is honest. One cannot be sly and shocked simultaneously.
—*Heart of the Original*

Got a call from her a year later. Asked where she was.
    "I'm in a hotel, like I said I would be. I'm in a hotel stuffing the piano with dollars. Bombers add to the amusement of the view."
    Good old Ruby. Let nothing part the web in her grave.
—*The Inflatable Volunteer*

But Gully Low was drowsing, a headache flower blooming in silence at his shoulder. His tea genie began seeping into view, fringed in shrivelling air.
—*The Complete Accomplice*

Laws clothe assault. Our soldiers will tear him limb from limb—and a man hates that.
—*Rebel at the End of Time*

"Screaming in a patient is to be expected," said Doctor Perfect. "Surgery done gingerly is mere infatuation."
—*The Complete Accomplice*

The smallest fly is shaped by all which surrounds it. Work to be ignored and you use the tendency of others' force—it's the subtlest martial art. Remember advice years after you ignored it and give thanks to your younger self.
—*The Nerve*

The first world war began with what was called "the excuse heard around the world."
—*Hyperthick*

In polarized times Herman Hesse's writing was like a window pane— those on either side saw their enemy in it.
—*Hyperthick*

Beguiling minutes I spent believing that it made sense. Then the realisation, and the anger.
—*The Complete Accomplice*

We have only the turnip of conformity to fend off our demons.
—*The Complete Accomplice*

Roy Christopher: Even with the blown-apart realities in your books, you have a real beef with postmodernism. Can you tell us a bit about this?

Aylett: I'm not so much bothered by the matter of literary postmodernism than by postmodernist notions as they're used in real life—where people carry those ideas over into the world, thinking that the words are the same thing as the object they label (that the map is the territory, contrary to Robert Anton Wilson's urging) and that the objects and facts can be shuffled and reorganised in the same way that their labels can be; including actual people. A lot of times this is harmless: if you give a muddy brick to a student of postmodernism and tell him it's the beer you just bought him, he should accept it with thanks. But human beings have a tendency to turn just about any philosophy into a justification for the manipulation of others, usually by re-labelling people as objects or lower-order creatures, which can then be furnaced or disposed of in any old way. But postmodernism doesn't even have to be subverted to those ends—it's the arch-philosophy of re-labelling and can be used to smooth the way for any atrocity or neglect, any sort of evasion of the real results of your actions. Look at the news and see hundreds of examples of this.

I do old-time satire in the Voltaire/Swift tradition. Real satire, by taking people's arguments (or evasions or justifications) to their logical extremes, snaps people back to the reality of the situation, i.e. that their evasions and justifications are cowardly bullshit. Of course it only works if there's a scrap of honesty in the reader to begin with, so it doesn't always work, and the way things are going socially, it'll work less and less. There'll be no honesty to appeal to, and no concept of that. There'll be no admission that there are facts and nobody will even remember the original motive for that evasion—that to deny that there's such a thing as a fact, means you can do anything to anyone without feeling bad about it. If you tell yourself they didn't feel what you did to them, they didn't feel it. To deny you did it means you didn't do it. Welcome to the swamp.

Hypocrisy won't exist in the future because hypocrisy requires an understanding of honesty as at least a concept. So satire will be a sort of inert, inoperative device which won't hook into anything.

I'm on a hiding to nothing, is what I mean.
—Interview (2004)

In heaven it's impossible to look the other way.
—*Hyperthick*

Pharaohs of ancient Egypt believed the heart was the seat of the intellect and had it wrapped separately.
—*Heart of the Original*

He seared his admirers with a volcano of modesty.
—*The Crime Studio*

Decypher something which wasn't encoded and you've scrambled it—
assuming deception, you've done the codemaker's job for them.
—*The Nerve*

A shame that the solutions to this world's problems are so lacking in
glamour. There are no explosions or big noises involved. They're not visually exciting. They're difficult to cover in short clips and soundbites. They
involve a different kind of revenge than the war kind—one that's quiet
and takes a million years. Patience and planning doesn't look plucky.
—*Lint*

System is irrelevant when those at the helm are fez-wearing toothfish
who treat their own principles like a bouncy castle.
—*Heart of the Original*

Gravity has a sure instinct for the dramatic.
—*Hyperthick*

They say a little embarrassment's good for you—I wonder what they
say about this much?
—*The Crime Studio*

There comes a point of exhausted exasperation at one's every act
meeting with blanket disapproval. The only sane course is to disengage.
—*Heart of the Original*

Though possessing three hearts, your common or garden octopus
doesn't show much courage when discovered and flees like Baudrillard,
obscuring its escape with a waste of ink.
—*Heart of the Original*

Hubris. We imagine the snow yearns for a footprint.
—*Hyperthick*

"Hell? But a man like me would be instantly toasted."
—*The Inflatable Volunteer*

Fain inspected bone bottles full of glass dust, bandaged toys with beaks, rusted autumnal fruit studded with nails, fragments of black honeycomb, an Ace of Hearts fossilized like a trilobite, an oversized sandtimer clotted fast with blood, a black rose on dark green velvet, and a skull of expertly fitted ebony and rosewood.
—*Fain the Sorcerer*

Euphoric corpses look to no saviour.
—*Shamanspace*

I devised a stepped September that went all the way down, a very deep month that could take years. Each gigantic hour was hung with throbbing rue fruit.
—*Hyperthick*

When he was at school Solitary had been chastised for a misbehaviour he did not commit, and while most of us would conclude from this that there is nothing to be gained from obeying the rules, Sol was more impressionable.
—*The Crime Studio*

Like all without power, he could have exchanged his philosophy with any one of his friends without its making the slightest difference.
—*Heart of the Original*

Three puppets seeing each other doesn't make them real, guys.
—*Hyperthick*

He's the mutant in society's boiler room.
—*The Complete Accomplice*

When I see what I've done so far I'm too pleased to apologize.
—*Lint*

The sea is a gigantic chemistry experiment.
—*Novahead*

A superstition has arisen in theatreland that it is unlucky to mention *A Team Becomes Embers Together* by name, and so it is alluded to merely as "the stupid play."
—*And Your Point Is?*

Become yourself like a tap at last running clear.
—*The Complete Accomplice*

I knew books could see people around them, they ground their tiny teeth, tried to rattle like windows, stories to tell.
—*Shamanspace*

Lint knew that his use of originality as the basic building unit of a book would result in the perception of at least two different versions of the book among readers—the bifurcation would begin with readers who accepted and included diversity, and those who deemed difference an exception which need not be factored in. The first would perceive richness, the second emptiness, and perceptual graduation in between and beyond would aggregate from there.
—*And Your Point Is?*

A doll among the cobwebs in an abandoned half-car has brighter ideas in her head.
—*Heart of the Original*

If I really am powerless, how do I surrender?
—*Hyperthick*

A species which cannot stop lying and yet clings to the desperate insistence, in the face of all evidence, that there are really only seven stories.
—*Heart of the Original*

Bad luck is the shadow of a thing too cowardly to show itself from head to tail. Isn't it interesting that government will operate in the same way? Its crime is concealed from end to end by the "common good."
—*Novahead*

Billy's life of crime had begun in his late teens when he broke a bottle over a guy's head and was arrested for impersonating a cop.
—*The Crime Studio*

"What were you doing in Washington, Atom?"
    "Visiting my rights."
—*Toxicology*

The idea of black holes was put forward in 1783 by John Michell and in 1915 by Einstein. Global electromagnetic resonances were accurately calculated by Tesla in 1899 and by Schumann in 1952, upon which they were called Schumann resonances. Also lost to memory for several decades were Richard Semon's theories on the effective retrieval of memory, including the stimulation of a previous and similar memory imprint or "engram." An original idea will find no similar engram.
—*Heart of the Original*

Juggle your merits fast to make them look more numerous, or slowly to better hide your slack, empty face.
—*Toxicology*

Life was such an implacable apparatus I had to tackle it at the hinges.
—*Hyperthick*

Could have done a lot worse than have a silver-eyed demon rasp doom in your ear.
—*The Complete Accomplice*

Success in a zoo is still failure.
—*Lint*

Power receives power.
—*The Complete Accomplice*

He was clean as the gutter in a dictionary.
—*Hyperthick*

The blackleather desk in the foyer had, it seemed, been surgically re-moved from a bison.
—*The Crime Studio*

"Doesn't everyone's cock have a ribcage?"
—*The Inflatable Volunteer*

"They are creatures who know so little about their own motivations we have to fill it all in ourselves. But how does that help anything, if none of the thought processes we used to work it out are happening in their minds when they do it? If it derives from incoherence?"
—*Fain the Sorcerer*

The dharma would have you believe that you condemn others' faults because they reflect your own. In truth their behaviour is so alien as to be practically none of your business.
—*Hyperthick*

The cat knows the difference.
—*Lint*'s rebuttal to Schrodinger

It seems that great things cannot be consummated until all the lies about them have been heard, so let go.
—*Heart of the Original*

The mayhem had all the diversified and collaborative qualities of good improvised theatre and it wasn't surprising that the papers claimed not to understand it.
—*The Crime Studio*

Fitzgerald wrote a book that died soon after publication but continued to fool people because its hair and nails kept growing.
—*Heart of the Original*

A slogan with a future is a thief without parallel.
—*The Complete Accomplice*

Keep the light behind you and they won't see you're thinking. You might also pass off an original notion by prefacing it with "It's an old idea that …" or "It's a cliché that …" You've shunted it into the past, rendering it presumably banal.
—*Heart of the Original*

We were holed long ago—we escaped thru it.
—*Hyperthick*

Noting that the precedent system in Western law bore an identical structure to that of mental neurosis, he had written a thesis on *Crime as a Creative Medium* and been kicked out bodily by a principal of such frail health Leon himself had had to support him during the procedure.
—*The Crime Studio*

They'll be stamping my features onto coins the size of manhole covers.
—*Bigot Hall*

Most books are reposts.
—*Heart of the Original*

She once rubbed a sleep crumb out of her eye and when I studied it under a microscope I found it was a perfect miniature replica of an Alpine village.
—*The Crime Studio*

People are often corrupted by their desire for power or wealth. Has anyone ever been corrupted by their desire to be left alone?
—*Heart of the Original*

Chose a point halfway through a funeral to abandon his trousers as a bad bet.
—*The Complete Accomplice*

Since your absurdities challenge themselves, I won't exert myself.
—*Hyperthick*

The "pragment" had been the beginning of Lint's habit of inventing words. By now he was having stories rejected for his use of words like "spile" (bitterness on a wet, yellow-colored day), "spagran" (gangly stranger with probable unhealthy habits) and "trun" (stubborn out-thrust of chin upon almost facing the truth). One unused story began "Walking out, I felt a pang of spile" and goes on to describe a spagran who, upon being observed, gives it a "bit of trun."
—*Lint*

Nature can get away with anything.
—*The Complete Accomplice*

He had honed his villainy to such an art he was practically innocent.
—*The Crime Studio*

Arrive in a stupid badger-faced biplane with five adrenalin pens hanging off your forehead. Arrange for your arms to be already windmilling as you enter a room, if possible knocking out the teeth of a spoilt child. Retrieve a hemisphere of flowing mercury from your inside pocket and gaze at it in an attitude of ferocious, twelve-bore self-pity.
—*Heart of the Original*

The play was made quite famous by a headline misprint in *Variety* reading OBSCENE PLAY ATTRACTS MASSIVE CROW.
—*Lint*

Among Lint fans the term "flirting with McCoy" is used in regard to someone who is not taking the situation entirely seriously.
—*Lint*

They were the biggest morons this side of the fossil gap.
—*The Crime Studio*

He went into the woods for the exclusive purpose of killing anything larger than his brain.
—*Bigot Hall*

In this land, reason hides for generations like a recessive gene.
—*Toxicology*

To them you may appear as radioactively terrifying as an angel. A price to be paid for individuality is the abandoning of approval.
—*Heart of the Original*

"I'll have plenty of time to be fashionable after I'm dead."
—*Lint*

A toxic beauty who had perfected the "wasted angel" look to such a pitch that people shielded their eyes against the expected atomic blast of her ascension. Chemically she was more than human.
—*The Crime Studio*

Like the compound eye of an insect, a compound brain can focus on a bunch of things at once. This allows the mind to perform a fractal dive, pouring through everlasting data assemblages, each level a *wimmelbild* or teeming scene with equal detail everywhere. In this order of operation, pattern recognition is easy.
—*Heart of the Original*

A stranger to joy, I had eked out my only endorphin by feeding it through a mangle.
—*Bigot Hall*

Humanity's abhorrence of common sense has a similar quality to that afforded originality because it, too, is a departure from familiar circumstance. The relatively reasonable Greek statesman Solon let himself down by making it a crime to publicly express political neutrality and also a crime to publicly speak ill of the living or dead, in the great tradition of combinatory laws which do not allow people to quite exist.
—*Heart of the Original*

Proving each of them wrong is dumb as snapping icicles.
—*Hyperthick*

All it needs is an Igor with a strong arm and the floorhatch lifts, belching smoke from the underlab. "That's what's missing round here," Eddie said, "a real, quality hunchback for your money."
—*The Inflatable Volunteer*

The Riding On Luggage Show tested musical stage conventions and salted the soil so densely that anyone purporting to do anything interesting in the future had to pretend that *Luggage* had never happened.
—*And Your Point Is?*

Moby Dick is Melville's long, uproarious explanation of why everyone jumped in the water.
—*Hyperthick*

Unable to regard the planning office with alarm or respect, Father had once designed a tower block which, during the official opening, shed a series of false walls to reveal a building which was quite pleasing to the eye. The embarrassed authorities finally faked a terrorist attack to remove the anomaly.
—*Bigot Hall*

"Society and its intricate array of dramas—we can take a direct or indirect road among these trivialities, but we will be among them, wasted and annoyed. Don't be a sap. You're being used. I'm saying, don't be a sap."
—*Novahead*

The gargantuan quantity of fact and consequence denied and evaded by human beings must go somewhere, and may constitute dark energy.
—*Heart of the Original*

Unable to lie, he turned the disadvantage on others like a flamethrower.
—*Hyperthick*

We arrived here fish-first and cannot know what is or is not a favorable mutation.
—*Hyperthick*

Failsafe became obsessed with that transition point at the border, where one barrage of restrictions gave way to another. Was there a point between the two—however minute—where neither were present?
—*Toxicology*

Anyone who has actually broken official protocol will know that at best it sends its agents into a sort of contentless whirl which does not have the vibrancy of honest panic, nor even that of genuine surprise—they seem merely to swerve from familiar bureaucratic rails onto some of the minor, less used branches of evasion. Nothing is ever changed, admitted or learnt. Yet in the world of "The Retrial" some effect can be had, perhaps by the sheer diagonal intensity of K's responses. Consider the cathedral scene—while you or I might merely windmill our arms and puff our cheeks out a bit, K. delivers a roundhouse to the priest by detonating into a perfumed cloud of dandelion seeds and buff-coloured smoke. The priest, who had been "smiling like a warship" only seconds before, now crouches on the floor like a spider, "karking and keening"— he seems to have been both deafened and confused by the blast.
—*And Your Point Is?*

Nothing's harder to exude than respect. Tends to come across as constipation.
—*The Complete Accomplice*

Whenever one of us entered the village, women swept children from the street, bicycles were abandoned, windows were slammed shut and ineffectual shopkeepers stood armed and apprehensive in doorways. But today this was raised to the tenth power—I felt like the previously unseen mutant child of a newly-defiant workman. One villager lobbed a lump of garlic, which I caught in my mouth.
—*Bigot Hall*

"Laws are backed by violence. Why else would anyone obey them?"
    "Out of reasonableness?" the Orchid ventured.
    "When they are backed by violence?" Brannart scoffed.
—*Rebel at the End of Time*

"The future's fucked. There are too many masks in the egg."
—*Lint*

She slapped me, twice. The first slap knocked the cigarette out of my mouth, the second put it back.
—*Novahead*

Heaven must be missing a magistrate.
—*Hyperthick*

There you go, trying to unkink a tree.
—*Hyperthick*

Harpoon Specter argued for a sentence as light as a dandelion seed, pointing out that human body cells replace themselves every six months and that when such time had elapsed the authorities would be holding the wrong guy. To his surprise the court agreed and decided to gas Auto before such a transformation could occur.
—*The Crime Studio*

"The equational surface of the situation is misleading," Krill suggested. "You know the notion of freedom can be mapped over anything—that doesn't make it so."
—*Rebel at the End of Time*

Strife's made worse by pattern recognition. Predictability, you know.
—*Hyperthick*

If you continue with a broken chair, do you snub the truth or accept it?
—*The Complete Accomplice*

Like snowflakes, no two fistfights are the same.
—*The Complete Accomplice*

He died with all the fanfare of a wristwatch in a drawer.
—*Hyperthick*

A crocodile died for my satchel—
tearful ears of sedative
pierced a carapace
to leave a leering dead weight
and a hateful, glossy case.
—Fragment from "Ted Hughes' Schooldays" in *Bigot Hall*

"Everyone yelps when they've got a principle, Juniper, uncertain if it's a thorn or a medal."
—*The Complete Accomplice*

Lint enjoyed describing the textured oasis around him, the white-noise ethanol sky, hot tin chassis in weeds and the crinkled feeling of tree. "A spider like a shiny bead, eyelashes growing from the side of a wall, a pressing heat before thunder relieves the sky."
—*Lint*

There's so much trouble in the world flies ought to be praised for being small enough to ignore.
—*The Inflatable Volunteer*

In school I was hollowed out like gangbusters. I emerged from their con-gratulations a beaten animal.
—*Hyperthick*

Death stares at our wrath like a babe at an equation.
—*The Complete Accomplice*

"Oh darling, we're really married."
  "And the dog makes three."
—*The Complete Accomplice*

I thought of people's strange reactions to the oldster who'd long since shucked his shell after apparently flouncing off in a sort of creative tantrum. Wisdom is not contagious.
—*Rebel at the End of Time*

"Can't change a circle to a square without reducing its surface area, laughing boy."

"What about a cube."

"You mar my argument by no more clever means than an increase in dimensions."

"To no greater number than that in which normal people move and have their being, Sideshow—it's not my fault your crap argument hasn't the stamina to exist in the real world."
—*Bigot Hall*

The Fadlands are a blandness its inhabitants subdivided to keep themselves busy.
—*Novahead*

Seeing the underpinnings of the world at all times, he finds himself to be terribly frank and unpopular wherever he goes.
—*And Your Point Is?*

The populace and its inexhaustible capacity for assent had to have a back end. Subjected to every sort of check and exhaustion, humiliation and indulgence, they sought alternative injustices, at least.
—*Novahead*

I glanced about me and considered all I could do here with a match and a scrap of courage.
—*The Inflatable Volunteer*

"You should look at each case on its individual merits. We can't comment on individual cases."
—*The Promissory*

In this story the inhabitants of Earth welcome extraterrestrial visitors with insincere, uncomprehended platitudes, dismal jokes and music. The tentacular visitors may be seen on occasion not only to vomit copiously, but also to become violent for the first time in their near-eternal lives.
—*And Your Point Is?*

Death? I've been hearing about that daunting transition for so long, I hope my boredom has been worth it.
—*Novahead*

I remember the days it began to get hot around here. It changed everything. Instead of being broken up in sharpness and rain, the land became heated like one large room. Tropicalia was a fashion for a while, then people had to deal with it for real. The chill was an old excuse for separation. And so a thousand new excuses were found.
—*The Complete Accomplice*

I bowed to his judgment so fast his nose broke.
—*Toxicology*

They were passing over wounds a century wide.
—*Rebel at the End of Time*

Cannon grabbed his shirt and tore it with a convulsive shriek.
   "Why have you rent your clothes?" asked the judge wearily.
   "Because I didn't want to rip my own."
—*Bigot Hall*

Of course if I dropped dead Eddie would have been first to steal my hair, the ideas at their root, my clothing, money, women, music, words and reputation. Then he'd start saying I did the murders. Then it would be dog-rogering practices and the poisoning of badgers he would charge me with as I lay cross-armed in the ruffled silk. Praying at the dark far rear of his head my eyes don't spring open and my purpling mouth demand the evidence.
—*The Inflatable Volunteer*

Reality is only half-done—but the coincidences are piling up.
—*Johnny Viable*

Sanity's a virginity of the mind.
—*Atom*

Employment keeps you occupied during the period of your life when you might be doing something useful.
—*The Complete Accomplice*

There persists a notion that humanity will learn lessons as a result of the upcoming collapses and that human denial has a limit (a notion mentally sustainable only because it doesn't).
—Preface to *The Complete Accomplice*

With every second that passed he was losing weeks of discipline forged while breaking bricks with his eyelashes in the Shaolin Temple.
—*The Crime Studio*

Baying pursuers have always been the key to staying slim.
—*The Complete Accomplice*

People are expected to ask themselves "Who am I?" and earnestly pretend they don't know.
—*Heart of the Original*

Everything starts somewhere. Inside or outside?
—*Hyperthick*

"Advantages in operation, Eddie ventured into the traffic ..." And here I told a tale so full of wonder and magic I nearly blinded myself. Whole empires were rendered in fly-leg detail, mangrove domes sweating rain, enchantments nabbed amid the closed snores of the innocent, balloon-trousered princes punching like a girl, convict voyages to temperatures unknown, expensive wounds inflicted by nutters, dogs wearing lipstick, litter temples and sacrifice.
—*The Inflatable Volunteer*

"If you're such a country boy, Reactor, what does it mean when the cows lie down?"
    "That they've been killed for food."
—*The Complete Accomplice*

"The only way he'll enter heaven is climbing over the wall with a knife clenched between his teeth."
—*Novahead*

And the time I found an injured bird which, as I nursed it back to health, began to shout at me with increasing belligerence. When it had reached the point of screaming that I was an impotent moron, I deemed its recovery complete and threw it out the window. From that time to this the bird has stood on the sill staring silently at me with its unforgiving eye.
—*Johnny Viable*

Devisers of human deceit in different camps provide the language we speak.
—*Rebel at the End of Time*

The devilish hold self-contradictory positions so that people who argue against them must take up self-contradictory positions also.
—*Novahead*

He was everything I wanted to be—consistent, Japanese, heavy-set as a Bassett hound.
—*Bigot Hall*

Votive grenades, burnt-out church valves and other devotional gewgaws he proceeded to show to Leo with a kind of baffled pride. All the paraphernalia of faith—though to Volospion's mind the notion that faith should require paraphernalia seemed a contradiction.
—*Rebel at the End of Time*

One observer complained that "Gamete aims to open a terrifying depth under our steps, into which we fall like a seed."
—*Novahead*

Given drift and infinite time, nature blunders through some astonishing highlights.
—*Hyperthick*

A man was once tasked with creating something using only the stomach contents of a great white shark. The result resembled a kind of consultant. It's pathetic to have someone else's gut feeling.
—*Heart of the Original*

It was Billy's belief that there are some things that don't exist in retail reality—they exist in the reality of stealing or being stolen.
—*The Crime Studio*

Here knowledge was a hot potato passed on rather than downed and digested. Anyone who grew his own mind was diminished, voiceless and futile under lofty neglect, incinerative condescension and the derisive intimacy claimed by government.
—*Toxicology*

"Understood too late? Maybe don't wait." That's my motto!
—*Hyperthick*

They'll celebrate difference when there's no alternative. That's irony.
—*Hyperthick*

The only reward for keeping your soul is your soul, nothing else. And sometimes your soul can feel like a very small thing.
—*Hyperthick*

They assure us of the carefree invulnerability we felt as children, contrary to our accurate memory of the time.
—*The Complete Accomplice*

Most books are so well written they barely have any effect on the reader's senses.
—*Toxicology*

"I'd like to tell you about the time I rode on a dog and thought for a moment I was a better man than I am."
—*The Inflatable Volunteer*

You can spark a fire by banging two facts together. Regrettably it takes only one lie.
—*Rebel at the End of Time*

Wealth isn't susceptible to law.
—*Hyperthick*

Sky the colour of beer, my past muffled in my coatpockets. Storm scaffolds in volcanic wind. What could I do but frighten a night with goat angels and apparatus? How did others make a living? Filling out the beliefs of patients. Appearing fat as usual on the gangplank, dummies in the front row to make up the numbers. Scarring the lectern with dances. Travel agent—hammer flat the idea that adventures are accompanied by vomiting and you're on to something. Chef? "We found a great number of serpents in the cake." And that's the end of that. Dread's the same uniformed.
—*The Inflatable Volunteer*

A crossroads shouldn't be boring. But here we are.
—*Hyperthick*

She learnt to keep her eyes closed when crying, tears flowing under the skin and over the skull.
—*Shamanspace*

The world's dealers in belittlement and manipulation have never been able to keep up with the demand.
—*The Promissory*

We're hardwired to fear a growl from the undergrowth but not the smile of a liar.
—*Hyperthick*

The crime was an act of violence in the wrong direction, upward against the grain of hierarchy, and was thus being declared an especial abomination.
—*Rebel at the End of Time*

Pity the pet fish which has a name—Tony, or Pluto—right between the eyes. Then whatever it does will be seen as evidence of rueful personality—look at Tony, his fins unfurled, near the airbubbles. Look at Pluto, collecting the fishfood in his face. Hell in such a small space.
—*The Inflatable Volunteer*

He had swallowed media promises of a better life and then overstepped the boundary of etiquette by actually trying to secure one.
—*Toxicology*

Henry Blince was the only guy I knew who grew himself as a hobby.
—*The Crime Studio*

A throne like a reared-up crayfish tail hardly indicates impulse control.
—*Hyperthick*

Liking harm and safety in equal measure, he punched a gran and ran home, forgetting his keys, wallet, passport, incriminating photos and bottles of DNA for subsequent whole-body replication in a police lab—all this was found on the scene, where the gran was laughing with the honour of the meeting and clutching a hunk of his hair. The police pinned up a Wanted poster of Bob's face and head, and every dog who saw it fell instantly in love with him. "See," I smirked, nudging him with both elbows at once, "you're a pin-up my son."

"For dogs," he clarified, enraged.

"It's a start."

"Some are probably police dogs brother. Look at that one." And he pointed to the face of an alsatian which had appeared at the window, panting steam.
—*The Inflatable Volunteer*

Don't add to the truth. A horse without a rider is a horse.
—*Hyperthick*

The truth can be as hot and transparent as aniseed.
—*Rebel at the End of Time*

His last attempt to kill with a rifle had shattered the observation window of a Seaworld exhibit aptly entitled "Shark Encounter."
—*The Crime Studio*

And now he lay with his entire world filled with the pores of her skin, big as the bark of a tree. Heaven was in the close warm hairs on the back of her neck. Heaven was in her heart. He was always amazed that the best feelings could be so simple. It was truth like licking a stone. It simplified his reflexes. It was consoling; possible.
—*Rebel at the End of Time*

This misery is as familiar as my own teeth.
—*Hyperthick*

Behind my face do I respect you? Is the war declaration friendly in the envelope?
—*Toxicology*

"When you look while recalling the names of what you see … you're at best seeing to the limit of example. By casting off those names, you see further."
—*Fain the Sorcerer*

Lord save us from those who are smartest at their elbows.
—*Hyperthick*

Common sense as a martial art, triangular language and the alphabet hidden beyond "Z."
—*Novahead*

"If all governments were combined, we could save on travel and gunpowder."
—*And Your Point Is?*

Leverage is dulled on a soft man.
—*The Complete Accomplice*

In a vacuum society, individual expression will have about it a contrary etheric which also works against the individual—if he wants to be noticed, he won't be; if he wants anonymity, he'll be stared at at every turn. Occupational hazard of being always in negative.
—*Novahead*

As one who will of necessity learn the art of conversation from his enemies, an honest man must be careful to note when a word does not yet exist to express a situation.
—*Lint*

Inevitably the sharp articulations of the law sent people zigzagging to comply until, transfigured by exhaustion and contempt, they disengaged from the matter entirely.
—*Novahead*

The way virtual games were set up, you couldn't sniff a geranium without coming nose to nose with a growling dinosaur which meant business.
—*Toxicology*

People agree in a uniform swoon I don't believe. Wholeness is good 'n healthy. Unanimity gives me the creeps.
—*Hyperthick*

The spasmodic nature of democracy has a tendency to appear and disappear like a dismal clown who thinks he's funny.
—*Novahead*

They were sat around a fire, smoking cigars rolled on the thighs of baffled women.
—*Novahead*

Write three sentences and remove the middle one—often the deleted sentence is implied by the remaining material. This is great for satire, as when readers fill in the gap, they think it's their idea.
—*Heart of the Original*

"No fate, I say. Did Alexander's mother give birth to a statue?"
—*Hyperthick*

All night I thought about the specificity of love and shelter against the rolling blasts of everything else. Endless ambush.
—*Hyperthick*

If Armstrong was interesting he'd phonetically blur his assigned lines—"That's one small pecker, man—one tired leaker, and mine." He'd slam from the capsule roaring drunk. He'd skip across the sands like a fairy. He'd pretend to meet aliens and narrate false thrills amid non-existent domes of tessellated gold. He'd plant the Chilean flag. He'd wheelie and wreck that crappy car. He'd claim the whole thing was a movie set. He'd speak in seamless, uneditable profanity. He'd laugh without interruption. He'd rant bitterly against his mother. He'd scream at a pitch which blew the headphones off NASA control. He'd say everything in a thick French accent. He'd yell that his facemask was filling with snot and abruptly terminate transmission.
—*Toxicology*

"I've come up with a new alloy specifically formulated to waste people's time. You can stare at it for as long as you like, and then if you try to use it for anything, it breaks. Simple as that."
    "What are you calling it?"
    "Haven't decided. Law? Magic? Guarantee?"
—*Hyperthick*

The term "rifle among Oswald's possessions" passed into the evidence and report despite the fact that it was an order, not an evidentiary observation.
—*Lint*

"Reincarnation shifts us upward through the species and finally the dozen or so human lives allotted us. We're not allowed to remember our past lives or the lessons learnt there—a system so patently stupid a number of souls suicide out of each and every incarnation as a protest."
—*Toxicology*

I was annoyed that my principles didn't permit me to strangle you. When I said so you responded with the sort of outraged gasp that would have sounded essentially the same a hundred years ago.
—*Johnny Viable*

For centuries authority had thought to collapse the calculus of crime by pressing the centre of its gravity, until it realised this was also its own centre of gravity.
—*Novahead*

Believe it hot, sacred in your stomach, like the fire of something stolen.
—*Rebel at the End of Time*

Melody had once seen his body splitting open as he bleached out behind geysers of infrared, lightning in the blot of his mouth and angel blowback gusting stuff off the breakfast table. And as he reversed out of the human bandwidth he pulled depths into the house, furniture exploding into blurdust and splinters.
—*Shamanspace*

"We just had a visit from the police."
"Was anything stolen?"
—*Hyperthick*

Ideal thoughts teach us what we needn't expect.
—*The Complete Accomplice*

Pain can't be wounded.
—*The Complete Accomplice*

My dreams are full of others' impulses. Waking life is my only real chance.
—*Hyperthick*

Partial knowledge can polarise opinion. Scholars insist St. George didn't kill a dragon, which means either it never existed or it's still out there.
—*Heart of the Original*

An odd victory, to be always reliable.
—*The Complete Accomplice*

We were running from an electrical storm once, hell of a thing—a stunning, crackling uproar. And he began to swerve for no reason I could see. I didn't mention it at the time. But then I had an unwise fit of temper. "I'm suspicious about you changing course suddenly when we were running from the electric storm the other night." Well he finally confessed but I had to physically pull the words from his face. Apparently he was running and decided maybe it wouldn't be such a bad idea to act like he knew what he was doing.
—*The Complete Accomplice*

You can't run while you're kicking yourself.
—*Novahead*

A book may assemble a grammar that puts the world into bejewelled order, providing arcane nourishment or the charged sense of being an instant on the real road.
—*Heart of the Original*

Stem had a somewhat haphazard face. In his place I would have covered it with a beard but he'd opted for several moustaches.
—*Toxicology*

God was seen as the great anatomist madman. Its tantrums are subterfuge. How could they be otherwise if it's all-powerful?
—*Rebel at the End of Time*

I sent *The Crime Studio* to William Burroughs to ask him to do a blurb comment for the back cover. A week later, he was dead.
—Interview (2004)

When asked why he was feeling so sorry for himself he answered without deceit that it was a result of looking objectively at his situation.
—*The Crime Studio*

A week to worry, another to pine, a third to know we've wasted our time.
—*The Complete Accomplice*

A life lesson: tanks are faster than you think.
—*Novahead*

I mime amid the crows and fog,
Concluding with a groan—
The only watcher was a dog
Whose snout was dripping foam.
—*Bigot Hall*

Remote and fuzzy—why fear the Sasquatch?
—*Hyperthick*

The hero in Lint's story "Bless" awakes one morning to find that he has no tentacles. Alarmed, he dashes out to discover that nobody else has any tentacles either and all claim in bafflement never to have had any. As Michael Hersh has observed, the metaphor points up "a moral or ethical sensibility which, unheld and unrecognized by anyone else on the planet, is not communicable." In most Lint stories this sensibility is that of honesty and independent thought.
—*And Your Point Is?*

Morality? They wear the notion like a wig.
—*The Complete Accomplice*

You're using your own brain as a bucking bronco.
—*Hyperthick*

A dolphin can blink his nose, and that's just the start.
—*Hyperthick*

Reality is discarded from the law like the marble chipped away to reveal a statue.
—*Novahead*

And so I lay back and close my eyes. Or as I call it, battle stations.
—*Hyperthick*

"Hell again?" Haft remarks to the vicar. "This religion of yours is a firetrap."
—*Lint*

"It was … what was it?" Jagged flicked through history, finding the page. "A life of wretchedness and resolution. Strength and lament. Barred from life by an apparently insurmountable honesty, that was the story in retrospect. And it says: 'In the presence of injustice his seditious nature revealed itself like security paint under fluorescent light.' That's not bad, is it? You disappeared before you could become entirely your opposite."
—*Rebel at the End of Time*

You've listed my attributes for the last time!
—*Hyperthick*

Some say he imploded, taking half the furniture with him as he reversed out of existence. Some say he became a black smoke which creeped over the walls and ceiling, dropping dead ants upon the assembly. Others report that he simply crawled away on his hands and knees, snickering like an evil barber.
—*Bigot Hall*

"Pathetically pissed-up and pretending otherwise."
  "Sweats like a kettle when thinking of the future."
  "Says he never dreams but shrieks before dawn."
  "In curlers all day and eyes in a jar."
  "No mind, beacon for academe."
  "Pounded jellyfish with heavy stone."
  "That's when his mother knew he was a bad 'un."
  "Wet behind the heart."
  "Unashamed and dull."
  "Mock tears, permanent and crywolf."
  "Promises shattered, debts forgotten."

"Doubt all, believe nothing."
"Wrecks the match with Kraut melodies."
"Click of a bone when he raises the pint."
"Says he knows horses and I bet he does."
"Plays the piano and won't admit it."
"Boiling blush when you mention cattle."
"Falls on the ground when you punch his face."
"Beckons kittens into horror."
"Snips off the tongues of sparrow chicks."
"Upper storey of his courage."
"Whacked to climax with a bible belt."
"Forbidden delights of antlered skull."
"New cement floor in basement."
"Bell jar in kitchen."
"Magnifying glass in toilet."
"Murder between meals."
"Birds' underwear."
"Eats dogfood."
"Eats dogs."
"Money and no job."
"Death and no body."
"Sex and no women."
"Cuttlefish and no parrot."
"Grew green beard."
"There's horror, brothers."
"Cheers."
—*The Inflatable Volunteer*

"I find both naively charming and horrifying the constant emphasis on postmodern subjectivity in our modern world, while those authorities who encourage and profit by that trend in the populace privately covet the hard facts."
—*And Your Point Is?*

Art never won any wars, nor started any.
—*Heart of the Original*

Our journey to the interior in wine-colored pants left us dumbstruck. Shem was done to death by a runaway lamb, I suffered catastrophic chin failure and Jack torpedoed his liver with a toxic sausage.
—*Hyperthick*

Sticking out of the doorknob was a smaller doorknob. Then the adventure ...
—*Hyperthick*

"I love you."
    "This isn't about you, Barny."
—*The Complete Accomplice*

I wish I could punch the scales from your eyes.
—*The Crime Studio*

Everything here will become edible—because I'll make it so. I'll need nothing more expert than a trowel, a flirting badger, ten skills I don't possess, a fable recited from memory, a kennel the size of an aircraft hangar and a bagel which speaks.
—*The Inflatable Volunteer*

Every empire's so precariously established, the most that can be hoped for is documentation.
—*Hyperthick*

A civilisation doesn't end spectacularly; it implodes into stink.
—*Novahead*

Even warring idiots generate a story, like crabs in a barrel.
—*Hyperthick*

Jeff Lint said in interview that many authors' creation of "understandable" characters who are a kind of "hollow" each reader was supposed to occupy, soon left him aggravated as a reader: "I will want to turn left and the character will turn right; I would ignore but the character obeys;

I would destroy an argument but the character is blandly convinced and wastes years of his life. As a reader I find myself locked within an automaton I cannot control, which will never do what I would do (even by chance), and which provides no nourishment."
—*And Your Point Is?*

He slammed his face unexpectedly against nocturnal windows and stayed there, as sinister and inconvenient as a fiend.
—*Bigot Hall*

"Every ten seconds somewhere in the world, someone is realising I'm right."
—*Lint*

"We raised an agent from scratch. Lived in a monastery and so on, and died unaware he was a virus—to sneak him into heaven. He'd then be activated and do the hit. But they found the heart of the creature wasn't there—this 'heaven' was just a place to get people squared away, one of countless infinite bandwidths for etheric soul material."
—*Shamanspace*

"He's got a sort of hen, out back. It's what he uses for a conscience. It's probably not much good."
—*Novahead*

Empire is superficial in all but its inequalities, with an inclination to falsehood and the menacing potency of arbitrary law, enlisting its own citizens to patch and maintain the illusion of their freedom. Claiming more for it does it a disservice.
—*Rebel at the End of Time*

The idea that being on the good side, and even winning, will save us ...
—*Hyperthick*

Satire has no effect—a mirror holds no fear for those with no shame.
—*And Your Point Is?*

"If we dealt honestly, maturely with our horrors," he told the purple-haired clown hosting a public access slot, "instead of evading, rejecting and forgetting, the energy of these events would be naturally reabsorbed. But as it is we have treated it as we treat our nuclear waste—and where we have dumped it, it is not wanted. The most recent waste will be the first to return."
—*Toxicology*

May time deny thee glory and grant thee peace!
—*Rebel at the End of Time*

"I wept lard this morning as I thought of how vexing and costly it will be for you. Then I carved the lard into the shape of a raven. So you see how I put you people first? Nothing is wasted. I save on expense by shrugging with only one shoulder. Get a loada this—heyup!"
—*The Complete Accomplice*

Most of the world operates within one or other subspecies of fascism. With so much consciously denied, nightmares are to be expected.
—*The Caterer*

You dabble in reality like an amateur surgeon and leave as much damage.
—*Hyperthick*

If a mere clock can be wrong, think what an inventive man can be!
—*Hyperthick*

"I have pondered the matter and decided that you and I shall be friends."
   "And when will this feeling grip me? I have a busy schedule."
—*The Complete Accomplice*

"I'll not fight with you, nor your male equivalent."
—*Fain the Sorcerer*

Life shoots first.
—*Atom*

An arrangement of stale certitudes remained roughly where they had been placed. The fossil light of these inherited notions was not enough to see by. For many it was a loss of clarity, a collapse of contrasts. People's coping mechanisms varied. Like anyone unable to originate their own character, the cops had joined the army. For others their determination to find it all unfathomable must have put a lot of strain on the mechanisms of dismay.
—*Novahead*

"I met that girl of yours—Amy. She was out there snogging a flower. I asked her its name and she said she didn't know. You young people today, eh?"
—*The Complete Accomplice*

In an eternal universe, any ending to a story is artificially imposed. Let's have a party.
—*Johnny Viable*

The closed symmetry of injustice is preferred to the ventilative release of justice because the former lasts longer.
—*Rebel at the End of Time*

In "Can We Please Move On?," human expressions finally turn around and refuse to cooperate with people's stupid reactions.
—*Lint*

A successful sin should make a difference, shouldn't it?
—*The Complete Accomplice*

As a protection at street level the law is a rumour, a phantom—ghostly until invoked, and invoked only after the harm has been done.
—*Novahead*

"Do you believe in the transmigration of souls, Mr. Thermidor?"
   "Eh? No."
   "Then I'll thank you to keep your opinions to yourself."
—*Atom*

The only puzzle worth doing is one which notices when it's solved—
something is activated.
—*The Complete Accomplice*

A court appearance is a sort of barn-raising but for a pal's alibi.
—*Hyperthick*

Threatening to burst—that's a complex dynamic.
—*Hyperthick*

His skull already made him a human. Why did he have to learn the behaviour?
—*The Complete Accomplice*

"What's wrong with a government?"
    "Well at the very least I have to get some scouts behind it or it's a
blind spot."
—*Rebel at the End of Time*

Thank god for the corner where I'm ignored.
—*Hyperthick*

"Redeeming your exploits by slamming a moral template over 'em like
a sandwich toaster eh?"
—*The Inflatable Volunteer*

Times Square, a sort of crossroad processing upwards of a million idiots
a day.
—*Lint*

I wish I had a fiver for every time I earnt a fiver.
—*Bigot Hall*

Obeying every law means submitting to chaos. And obeying only some,
of course, still means submitting.
—*Novahead*

Stop looking for answers in artificial grass.
—*Hyperthick*

A spud in a fez is as good as a guru.
—*Hyperthick*

If I take a cross-section of the truth, do I get half? Or a hair's width?
—*Hyperthick*

The moment when death, without anger or consent, strolls though us.
—*Johnny Viable*

So how did Eddie end?
    Loafing a failure at the table?
    Feeding his eyes on climbs of fields from a dungeon window?
    Riding his cloak in huge winds?
    Gnashing cigars in smokelaze and stabbing cards at a table?
    Riding confusion to the army, caterpillar fists curving corners on flag-day?
    An extravagant death on the roof of the world?
    Stumbling after the lost and damned, a buccaneer to nowhere in deserts of uniform?
    Alone with the skeleton of a sandwich and his deal with dread?
    Drugshop eyes all pause, hours enchanted, answering one thing forever?
    Asleep in the rising moon to know that strange glory?
    Chairsad in soupmanners?
    Onward in poison?
    Divine to the gallows?
—*The Inflatable Volunteer*

It was such a boring debauch I walked out before I was even tired.
—*Hyperthick*

Careful. A uniform is a dice.
—*Smithereens*

He believed he had brilliantly transferred his mind to a position behind my face. Ghoulish notion!
—*Johnny Viable*

She refined her own ore without allegiance, a sort of blazing innocence that shrivelled the curtains and popped the windows, jetting flame into the alley. Now read on!
—*Hyperthick*

It seems you've been busy as the skin of a corpse, young lady!
—*Hyperthick*

This world, all of it clashing from end to end. I love the quenching acid drench of resistance, futile or otherwise. It's mine like the tingling ridge of a scar.
—*Hyperthick*

Why be awed by the immensity of obstacles and not by the immensity of nature?
—*Novahead*

They'll raise badly-rendered statues to me in this town and rendering mills for you in the next.
—*The Caterer*

Once again his career as a boneless striver had left him entirely unprepared to face the day.
—*The Complete Accomplice*

I suspect it is a puzzle unintelligible to any but the infinitely humorous.
—*Rebel at the End of Time*

You may have reserves of irreverence deeper than the ocean, and it is nothing without a palisade to work against. Better not to use another as a reference point.
—*Hyperthick*

"It has crossed my mind—on skis, as a matter of fact."
—*Atom*

All will be lost, its controversy and context.
—*Hyperthick*

His understanding goes deep, but only in one location.
—*Rebel at the End of Time*

"You can fence?"
  "I learnt when I was angry."
—*Novahead*

A shooter went forth to shoot, and when he shot, some bullets went by the wayside, growing nothing. Some went upon stony places, growing nothing. Some went among thorns, growing nothing. Others went into good ground, growing nothing. And others went into soft flesh, growing nothing. He who has ears, let him hear.
—*Novahead*

At his death Lint was working on something called the Vermilion Equation, by which almost bottomless amounts of retrievable information could be sunk into minute bits of text. The equation seems to hinge on the notion that nothing is so strange it can't be true. Adjunct to his calculations were mandala-like schematics resembling the paintings of Paul Laffoley. One is labelled "The Alontvashid. This particular page. In the shuffle of eternity even this was once perhaps the flushed centre of something."
—*Lint*

The body fools the mind and heart into facing in only one direction at a time. Truth is not separate or elevated—it inhabits the same space, like water in water. As much of it is behind us as in front. An animal like a dolphin with eyes on either side of its head and a large enough brain will think in several directions at once by experiencing an expanse rather than a line of direction.
—*Heart of the Original*

Wild proof, a staggering result!
—*Hyperthick*

Kindness is beyond appeal; simple. Today it's like an alien substance, too subtle and quiet to collide with anything.
—*Novahead*

He prodded a finger into each eyesocket and drew off his skin like a rubber hood—the skull beneath was smoothly ribbed like a moulded jelly basin. "*Here*'s what I have to contend with all day every day." He began pulling on the headglove again. "The more distraction there is from *this* little nightmare the less crap I have to take from narrowminded bigots."
—*The Inflatable Volunteer*

To reach the point of being unexploitable may be a long quest or a short one.
—*Hyperthick*

Bork has observed that "the taboo position of honestly-admitted power-lessness blasts a purifying light through Lint's novels." This allows Lint's protagonists to start a tale with an accurate view of the circumstances to be confronted (a point which other authors' protagonists rarely reach by the end). Critics have complained that Lint's stories lack conflict—they do, in fact, conflict with every story written by everyone else.
—*And Your Point Is?*

"None of us will ever admit to knowing what you mean."
—*Hyperthick*

A rare gift of dotage—either bitter or sweet depending on how much external influence you accepted—is the suspicion that you were actually right all along.
—*Novahead*

Those who didn't understand it apologised on its behalf.
—*Heart of the Original*

Ghosts were involved in the enterprise but only because they could wraith around the oven door and make it look like cooking-smoke without us using energy or food during the baking process. In fact that was the lynchpin of the whole deal. How could I be such a fool?
—*The Inflatable Volunteer*

Temples of prejudice and schools of hysteria, every textbook a funeral mass for an idea.
—*Rebel at the End of Time*

Beerlight rules for Russian Roulette. A group of people sit around a table on which rests a fully loaded gun. The first one to pick it up and shoot himself is the Russian.
—*The Crime Studio*

Got tired of forever waking up with bits of puzzle stuck to my face.
—*Novahead*

Don't whack a pinata if you don't want candy.
—*Hyperthick*

"Mr President," said Atom through the clench of his grin, "the day that Memorial statue of Abe Lincoln looks aside with a great wrench and steps down like a Harryhausen giant, your balls are pancakes."
—*Atom*

"Break your own heart—I'm busy."
—*Atom*

A tree grows in theory and in practice.
—*Hyperthick*

Luck is energy. Both good and bad luck exist. And, like energy, neither can be created or destroyed. We find ourselves chosen by stings in a boundless ocean.
—*Rebel at the End of Time*

It was some days before the facts were established. The trickster Prancer Diego had caused bloody havoc in the Square by releasing a parrot directly into a gran's face. The traumatised old woman had run amok, climbing a tower and hurling years of stored abuse upon the town. Condensed and purified over time, her scorn was so meticulous it had caused everyone alive to black out for forty minutes.
—*The Complete Accomplice*

I wanted to remove her skulltop and slather my tongue through her brainfolds.
—*Bigot Hall*

The hook-throne of approval ...
—*Lint*

Tell the truth or be transformed into the average man.
—*Lint*

Reputation? I have my nightmares for that.
—*Hyperthick*

Beginners in spatial thinking can write an idea, put it down and walk away while acknowledging all the adjacent ideas they're wading through—keeping a continuity of mind down the street and round the bend leads fairly soon into vivid territory.
—*Heart of the Original*

Some wait to be discovered—others, to be found out.
—*The Complete Accomplice*

"Bastard. Wore gym shorts to a funeral. Berated him later and he said, 'Yes I wore shorts—that's why I understood the jeering.'"
—*The Inflatable Volunteer*

That's as obscure as an embalmer's answer.
—*Lint*

"With freedom comes responsibility," he bellowed. "And since we are not free, we act irresponsibly. Yet our masters feign shock and disappointment. Be proud of me now—I take full responsibility for this!"
—*Rebel at the End of Time*

She swallowed a faulty penny twist that had been turned thru an extra dimension.
—*Hyperthick*

Her soul filled the air like solvent.
—*Slaughtermatic*

"Here's a riddle for you: I am not mad—nor do I possess reason. I whisk bones and bodies in the chill. A modest cash subsidy will not deter me. I may wear a hat for a short time. I retreat, leaving clammy horrors. What am I?"
   "A chef."
   "The sea, you moron, the sea!"
—*The Complete Accomplice*

"Stood on forecastle, watching sunset. Perhaps I am becoming a broken man."
—*Smithereens*

Eternity, my favorite!
—*Hyperthick*

When the abyss gazes into you, bill it.
—*Lint*

Revelation too late. Keys past, useless but for a stranger's door.
—*The Complete Accomplice*

"My deepest contradictions are of one accord when compared to you alien fucking smithereens."
—*Novahead*

"I've been purified."
  "How?"
  "By disgust."
—*Rebel at the End of Time*

In 1970 an interview with Lint appeared in *IT* and Lint spoke about the connection which occurs between two disparate objects "via the billion billion intervening forms which the two objects are not—the trip between those two objects, even if they're just a spoon and a salt shaker here on this table, really is a trip." The same was true of two ideas—if Lint was presented with a choice between two philosophies, he would see the billion billion other philosophies between those two, "and then those extended outside that created line, and in all other directions. In other words, there are options."
—*Lint*

A frangible philosophy exploded on impact, leaving numerous fragments around the brain.
—*Novahead*

Squinting at binaries has wrecked my eyes.
—*Hyperthick*

Everyone gets home a different way. You won't get home someone else's way.
—*Hyperthick*

Meeting with your life takes years, an accidental meeting—it won't let you get away soon unless you're firm with it.
—*Novahead*

A truth which is biographical or more generally applicable?
—*Hyperthick*

Nemesis crush—one at a time please.
—*The Inflatable Volunteer*

Pretending you're unscathed is a wretched way to live.
—*The Aylett Tarot*

You take your life in your hands when you write one of mine. Should you look down at your own boots kicking through black coins, or up at the horizon patrolled by lies with bright yellow fins? Watched always by a red frog like a beating heart? The distractions are geometrically infinite, years of it receding. But you can leap over it. Riding on a lion whose jaws want you.
—*Smithereens*

The courage to call everything's bluff. To let it do what it's always threatening. Exhilarating consequence.
—*Hyperthick*

Acceptance—the lowlands of joy, close to gravity.
—*Hyperthick*

Knots rot.
—*Hyperthick*

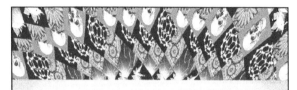

Heart of the Original
STEVE AYLETT

ORIGINALITY, CREATIVITY, INDIVIDUALITY

"A sizzling and hilarious manifesto where its author
means every blazing word" –ALAN MOORE

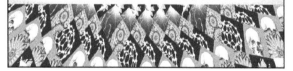

Look for me in the infinite reaches of my mistakes.

THE FOOL

STEVE AYLETT is the author of books including *Lint, Rebel at the End of Time, Novahead, Slaughtermatic, Heart of the Original*, and *The Complete Accomplice* as well as the comics *Hyperthick* and *The Caterer*. He lives in Scotland.

WWW.STEVEAYLETT.COM

Lightning Source UK Ltd.
Milton Keynes UK
UKHW042227010323
417781UK00004B/45